NOTES ON LOGIC

by

ROGER C. LYNDON
The University of Michigan

D. VAN NOSTRAND COMPANY, INC.
PRINCETON, NEW JERSEY
TORONTO NEW YORK LONDON

D. VAN NOSTRAND COMPANY, INC.
120 Alexander St., Princeton, New Jersey *(Principal office)*
24 West 40 Street, New York 18, New York

D. VAN NOSTRAND COMPANY, LTD.
358, Kensington High Street, London, W.14, England

D. VAN NOSTRAND COMPANY (Canada), Ltd.
25 Hollinger Road, Toronto 16, Canada

Published simultaneously in Canada by
D. VAN NOSTRAND COMPANY (Canada), LTD.

PRINTED IN THE UNITED STATES OF AMERICA

A false conclusion; I hate it
as an unfilled can.

— *Twelfth Night, II, 3*

PREFACE

These are notes from a course for advanced undergraduate and beginning graduate students in mathematics and related subjects which the author taught at the University of Michigan in the fall terms of 1962 and 1963. The attempt has been made to present the notes as simply as rigor permits, giving them something of the spirit of elementary abstract algebra. The subject matter, which can be seen from the Table of Contents, is all well known, and only occasionally have references been given.

The author wishes to state expressly his debt over many years to Alfred Tarski, with the hope that some of his ideas will be visible in these notes. The author is especially grateful to James Bennett for reading the manuscript.

R. C. L.

Ann Arbor, Michigan
1964

TABLE OF CONTENTS

INTRODUCTION

Logic is often said to deal with the laws of thought. Here is meant not the historical or psychological principles governing the process of thought, but rather those formal structural properties of thought which appear to reflect properties of the real world. We shall not enter here into the question of how such a connection between thought and reality is possible, but will proceed directly to study the possible formal nature of such a connection and its consequences.

One example is basic. Suppose that from a sentence p a sentence q follows by everyday reasoning. If we know that in fact p is true, we conclude that q also is true. Besides the obvious practical advantage of an awareness of the relation p implies q, there remains the possibility of using it to organize our knowledge and beliefs in such a way that we feel we have gained some understanding of the world.

A central theme will be the attempt to parallel the factual or *semantic implication relation*, $p \models q$, that if p is true then q is true, with a purely formal or *syntactical implication relation*, $p \vdash q$, that q is deducible from p by certain prescribed rules. A course of training in correct reasoning might simply lay down these rules and proceed to illustrate the various techniques for using them, leaving any critique of the correctness or usefulness of these rules to the reader's common sense. Our position is nearly opposite: we are greatly interested in the justification of our rules and in assessing their scope and limitations, but we shall try to avoid as far as possible all consideration of their technical details. We are less interested in the technical details of the deductive relation than in the interplay between semantic and syntactic concepts.

The formal study of any subject drawn from daily experience begins by replacing the everyday subject matter by suitable abstractly characterized idealizations, chosen to preserve those features of the original subject that are relevant to the study at hand. Here we need abstract substitutes for thought, for reality, and for the connection between thought and reality. For thought we substitute *language*, or, more precisely, a formalized version of parts of everyday language. It can be argued that all the purely formal aspects of thought are adequately reflected in such a language. For reality we substitute something called a *structure*, which is hardly more than a collection of things suitable for being correlated, as meanings, to various expressions in the language. For the connection between thought and reality we substitute an *interpretation*, that is, a function assigning to certain expressions in the language, as their meanings under the interpretation, certain objects in the structure.

We shall consider only a single language L, apart from some more or less minor variations in its details. What can be said in one reasonably adequate language can presumably be said in another. But we shall consider many interpretations of L in different structures S. This is partly because we do not know in which particular possible world, or structure, we actually find ourselves. It is more because, as logicians rather than empirical scientists, we do not care: logic is presumably concerned only with universal principles true in all possible worlds.

PROGRAM

Precise abstract definitions will be given later of the concepts of a language L, of a structure S, and of an interpretation ϕ mapping a language L into a structure S. We should like to make an analogy with the theory of groups, where one begins by defining a group, a vector space, and a representation mapping a group into transformations of the space. One usually continues with a purely formal study of some of the elementary properties of groups considered in isolation, then passes to the study of their representations, and in the end returns to derive from the representations further knowledge of the intrinsic properties of groups. Our program will be roughly similar. We shall begin with the grammar or elementary syntax of L, those properties of the language that deal with its formal structure and do not rely, except for their motivation, upon reference to interpretations. Next we consider the various interpretations of L; as indicated, the main result of this is the definition of the relation of semantic implication, $p \models q$, that q is true under every interpretation for which p is true. Finally we return to the study of the syntax of L on a more sophisticated level, and in particular to the study of syntactical relations $p \vdash q$ that approximate the semantic relation $p \models q$. This is our overall program, but we have not tried to force our exposition into any such strict outline.

We shall use the word *theory* in a technical sense. A theory is a language L together with a set T of sentences or formulas in the language. In practice, a theory is usually defined either semantically or syntactically: T may consist of all formulas of L that are true under each of a specified set of interpretations; or T may consist of all formulas that follow, under a specified relation of syntactic implication, from some given set of formulas, called *axioms*. In mathematics a theory that is primarily concerned with only a single structure, such as the theory of functions of a complex variable, is usually defined semantically, by reference to that structure; a theory concerned with a whole class of structures, such as the theory of groups, is usually defined syntactically, by axioms. But in mathematics the distinction is often blurred and shifting, and indeed this possibility of shifting from one approach to the other has proved extremely useful.

For the most part we shall be concerned with a single theory T in a fixed language L, and shall develop the theory of this theory. In the theory of theories there arises an ambiguity that does not arise in the theory of groups, and to clarify it we shall refer to the theory T being studied as the *object theory* T, in the *object language* L, and we shall refer to the theory in which we study the object theory as the *metatheory* T', in the *metalanguage* L'. The object language L will not be a language at all in the everyday sense, but a certain precisely defined abstract entity, designed to mimic actual language; and T likewise will be abstractly defined. On the other hand, as our metalanguage L' we shall take the language of ordinary mathematical discourse, a mixture of English with mathematical notation; likewise with T', we shall take as our axioms and methods of deduction those that are commonly employed in mathematics.

It is perhaps worth emphasizing this distinction. We shall specify the object language L and its theory T as abstractly and meticulously as we know how. But in the metalanguage L' and the metatheory T' that is, in reasoning about L and T—we shall try to avoid all pedantry and to be as informal as clarity permits. We take it for granted that the reader understands English and a few standard mathematical terms, and that he will accept a proof of a theorem of logic if it is presented with the same degree of rigor as is usual in the theory of groups.

Still a few remarks should be made about the relation of theory and metatheory. First, although there is no need to identify them, and it is confusing if not disastrous to do so, we must realize that the language L with its theory T arose as an abstraction from languages such as L' with its theory T'. There is therefore a natural urge to compare them, and this, as we shall see later, is highly rewarding. Second, it might be argued that the development of the properties of a language L within a metalanguage L', for which all the corresponding properties are taken as given, is peculiarly fruitless and circular. One may answer that the use of language to study language is no more profitless in mathematics than in philology, provided one does not read too much into it. When we define a sentence, *p and q*, to be true just in case both p is true and q is true, we are clearly not providing an analytical definition of the word *and*; and similar remarks apply to Tarski's more complicated definition of the truth of a sentence of L, although here it can be claimed that some insight has been provided into the role and internal structure of the concept of truth.

The word *metamathematics*, for the theory of mathematical theories, was introduced by Hilbert in his attempt to prove the consistency of a theory T, in a language L, that embodied a substantial fragment of classical mathematics. His idea was to show, by the study of the structure of formulas in T alone, that T could contain no contradiction. For such a proof of consistency to carry any force, the metatheory T' should be more modest than T, and indeed beyond question. It follows from a result of Gödel, which will be discussed later, that no such consistency proof is possible. Nonetheless, in view of the uncertainties which must therefore be attached to a strong metatheory, there is much to be said for conducting the study of L within the weakest metatheory that will serve. A "constructive" metatheory, by common consent beyond question, would serve for much of the syntax of L, but is unfortunately quite inadequate for semantical considerations, which require a free use of sets, functions, and relations. Therefore, as well as to simplify the exposition, we have taken as metatheory the strong, and not entirely clearly defined, theory traditional in mathematics. To put everything on a thoroughly precise basis, we could, following a suggestion of Lorenzen, axiomatize our metatheory T' in turn in a meta-metatheory T'', the latter to be constructive; but we do not undertake this here.

GRAMMAR

The differences between our language L and common English, at least as regards its structure as against the meanings we shall attach to it, are rather superficial. We shall use different symbols, and a different word order, borrowed from mathematics; in this we depart from English hardly more than does Latin or German. More important, the rules of formation for L will be utterly regular, and, in particular, no expression of L will admit more than one grammatical analysis.

The elements of a written language are expressions—letters, words, sentences, paragraphs—and among these are certain minimal expressions, or symbols—letters, including punctuation and spaces—with the property that every expression can be broken up in only one way into symbols, and that symbols cannot themselves profitably be analyzed further. There are in English and similar languages criteria, usually rather irregular in detail, for accepting certain expressions as grammatically well formed, and for dividing such expressions into various categories of nouns, verbs, phrases, sentences, and so forth. Although this part of grammar obviously is guided by the intended meaning, it is in principle quite independent of any reference to meaning.

The grammar of any existing language is necessarily largely descriptive and analytical, resolving expressions into symbols as their ultimate components. But for the purpose of constructing a new language L it is easier to proceed the other way, beginning with a set of symbols and defining the various categories and properties of expressions in terms of them. We begin with any abstract set S, whose members we elect to call *symbols*. We define an *expression* to be any finite sequence $e = s_1 \ldots s_n$ of symbols $s_1, \ldots, s_n$, and denote by E the set of all expressions. [Technically, we may prefer to view e as a function from the set of integers i such that $1 \leq i \leq n$ into S, with values $e(i) = s_i$.]

Grammatical analysis rests largely upon recognizing one expression as the product or concatenation of two others. We introduce a multiplication into E by defining the *product* ef of two expressions $e = s_1 \ldots s_m$ and $f = t_1 \ldots t_n$ to be $ef = s_1 \ldots s_m t_1 \ldots t_n$. [Technically, the function $g = ef$ is defined, for $1 \leq i \leq m + n$, by setting $g(i) = e(i)$ if $1 \leq i \leq n$, and $g(i) = f(i - n)$ if $n + 1 \leq i \leq n + m$.] It is clear that multiplication satisfies the *associative law:*

$$(ef)g = e(fg) \qquad \text{for all } e, f, \text{ and } g \text{ in } E.$$

A set E, equipped with an operation that satisfies the associative law, is called a *semigroup.*

In defining the set E of expressions $e = s_1 \ldots s_n$, we intentionally did not exclude the case that $n = 0$; there is a unique *trivial expression* e_0 of length 0. [It is more evident that there is one and only one way to define a function e from the empty set into S: we must take e also to be empty.] The trivial expression clearly satisfies the following law:

$$ee_0 = e_0 e = e \qquad \text{for all } e \text{ in } E.$$

A semigroup E with an element e_0 satisfying this law is called a *unitary semigroup.*

An element of a semigroup is called *prime*, or indecomposable, if it is not trivial and cannot be written as the product of two non-trivial factors; the primes in E are evidently the symbols. [Technically, the primes are the expressions consisting of a single symbol, rather than the symbols themselves, but for the time being there is no need to observe this distinction. Further, we have made the tacit assumption that no element of S is a sequence of elements of S: we do not regard the letter W as a sequence of two letters V.] It is also clear that E possesses the *unique decomposition property*: each e in E is representable as a product $e = s_1 \ldots s_m$ of primes, and if also $e = t_1 \ldots t_n$ where all the t_i are primes, then $m = n$ and $s_1 = t_1, \ldots, s_m = t_m$.

EXERCISES

1. Consider if there is something which might loosely be called a language, such as Morse code, vocal music, or painting, which (i) is not a semigroup; (ii) is a semigroup in which the unique decomposition property fails, either because not every expression is decomposable into primes, or because the decomposition is not unique; (iii) is a *commutative semigroup*, that is, one in which the law $ef = fe$ holds for all e and f.

2. Prove for the semigroup E the following theorems:

(i) $ef = gh$ implies either $e = gk$ and $h = kf$ for some k or else $g = ek$ and $f = kh$ for some k;

(ii) $ef = fe$ implies $e = g^m$ and $f = g^n$ for some g and some natural numbers m and n;

(iii) $e^2f^2 = g^2$ implies $ef = fe$.

3. If E and E' are semigroups, a map ϕ from E into E' is a *homomorphism* provided it preserves multiplication: $\phi(ef) = (\phi e)(\phi f)$. A semigroup E is *free* if it has a *basis* S, that is, a subset S such that any map from S into a semigroup E' has a unique extension to a homomorphism from E into E'. Show that this is equivalent to E having the unique decomposition property, with S the set of primes.

We begin now to specify the classification of expressions into categories, or parts of speech, starting with the symbols. For the language L with which we are henceforth concerned, we shall divide the symbols into ten categories. We do not care what these symbols are, so long as the categories are disjoint, but since we shall speak often about these symbols, we want fixed names for these categories. Seven of the categories contain a single symbol each; to each of these seven symbols we assign both an English name and a mathematical designation, as follows:

> falsehood symbol, 0; truth symbol, 1; negation symbol, N; conjunction symbol, C; disjunction symbol, D; universal quantifier, A; existential quantifier, E.

These seven symbols are the *connectives*. [Note that 0 has been introduced as the name of a symbol that we want to talk about; the symbol itself need not be of circular form, or indeed be a geometric shape at all.]

The three remaining categories will be called V, the class of *variables*; F, the class of *function symbols*; and R, the class of *relation symbols*. To each function symbol f we suppose attached an integer $\mathsf{n}(f) \geq 0$, the *rank* of f, and to each relation symbol r a rank $\mathsf{n}(r) \geq 0$. Alternatively, we could suppose F and R divided into infinitely many subcategories, F_0, F_1,... and R_0, R_1,..., according to rank.

We anticipate by giving a very rough indication of the meanings we intend to attach to these symbols. The symbol 0 can be read as standing for any false sentence, such as $2 \neq 2$, and 1 for any true sentence, such as $2 = 2$. For Np, Cpq, Dpq we shall read: not p, p and q, p or q (or both). If x is a variable, Axp means p is true for all x, and Exp that p is true for some x; if p is $7x > 5y$, Axp says of y that $5y$ is smaller than 7 times every number, and Exp that $5y < 7x$ for some x. The variables are usually taken as individual variables, denoting individual, unanalyzed objects, as against sets, functions, and so forth. Examples of function symbols of ranks 1 and 2 are, in ordinary notation, the symbols $\sqrt{\ }$ in $\sqrt{x}$ and $+$ in $x + y$. A function symbol of rank 0, or individual constant, depends on no arguments, hence denotes a fixed individual; examples are the synonymous symbols π and 3.14159.... Relation symbols of ranks 1 and 2 are Pos, if we write Pos(x) for $x > 0$, and $<$ in $x < y$. Relation symbols of rank 0 make assertions that depend for their truth on no arguments; they occur rarely in ordinary discourse, unless possibly as Conjecture C_3 or Hypothesis H_7.

TERMS

We shall consider, beyond symbols, only two main categories of expressions, terms and formulas. Terms will act as nouns and pronouns, being interpreted as naming objects in a structure. The variables will be so interpreted, and are therefore classed among the terms. We shall ultimately interpret a function symbol f of rank n by a function of n arguments from the structure and with values in the structure. If $t_1,\ldots,t_n$ are terms, naming objects in the structure, we shall take the expression $ft_1\ldots t_n$ as a term naming the value of the function named by f on these n objects. We shall take nothing more as a term except as follows from these conditions.

Precisely, we define the set T of *terms* to be the smallest among all sets U of expressions of L such that:

(1) $\mathsf{V} \subseteq U$,

(2) f in F_n and $t_1,\ldots,t_n$ in U implies $ft_1\ldots t_n$ in U.

To justify this definition we must show that there is some one smallest set T among all sets U satisfying (1) and (2). First, there exist sets satisfying (1) and (2), for example the set E of all expressions. Next, we observe that if we have any family $\mathcal{F}$ of sets U satisfying (1) and (2), and U_0 is the common part of all the sets of the family, then U_0 also satisfies (1) and (2). Now, if we take $\mathcal{F}$ to comprise all sets that satisfy (1) and (2), then U_0 is a set satisfying (1) and (2) and contained in every other such set.

EXERCISES

1. Assuming that there is exactly one variable x and one function symbol f, with $n(f) = 1$, describe explicitly the set of terms.

2. The same if $n(f) = 2$.

3. A variable x supplies one argument to a term: set $A(x) = 1$. A function symbol f of rank n consumes n arguments to give one argument in return: set $A(f) = 1 - n$. Show that if $e = s_1 \ldots s_m$ is a term, then $A(e) = A(s_1) + \ldots + A(s_m) = 1$, and characterize the terms e by means of the partial sums $A(s_1 \ldots s_i)$, $1 \leq i \leq m$.

4. Using Exercise 3, prove that $e = fg$ is possible for e and f both terms only in case g is the trivial expression.

5. Prove that if $ft_1 \ldots t_m = gs_1 \ldots s_n$ is a term, where f and g are function symbols and the t_i and s_j are terms, then $f = g$, $m = n$, and $t_1 = s_1, \ldots, t_m = s_m$.

6. Supposing that it can be told at a glance if a symbol belongs to V, or to F_n, for each n, devise as efficient a procedure as you can for checking whether a given expression is a term.

An *abstract algebra* consists of some non empty set A as *domain*, together with a set of *operations* w_i, each of some rank $n(w_i)$, indexed by a set I. Here an operation w of rank n is simply a function of n arguments from A with values in A. Two algebras A and A' are *similar* if they are indexed by the same set I, and if corresponding operations have the same rank: $n(w_i) = n(w_i')$ for all i in I. A map ϕ from A into similar A' is a *homomorphism* if for each i in I and all elements $a_1, \ldots, a_{n(w_i)}$ in A, one has

$$\phi[w_i(a_1, \ldots, a_{n(w_i)})] = w_i'(\phi a_1, \ldots, \phi a_{n(w_i)}).$$

An algebra A is *free* (with respect to its similarity class), with *basis* B, if B is a subset of A and every map from B into any algebra A' similar to A can be extended uniquely to a homomorphism.

We make the set T of terms into an *algebra of terms*, indexed by the set F, by defining operations $w(f)$ as follows: for all f in F_n and all $t_1,\ldots,t_n$ in T, we define

$$w(f)(t_1,\ldots,t_n) = ft_1\ldots t_n.$$

It can be shown that T is free with basis V.

EXERCISE. Prove this.

The concise notation $ft_1\ldots t_n$ has now served its purpose, and, except for emphasis, we shall employ now the more usual notation $f(t_1,\ldots,t_n)$ to name the same expression. Note that commas, parentheses, and triple dots are not part of the language L, or even names for expressions in L, but merely part of the conventional procedure for naming an element of L.

FORMULAS AND SENTENCES

The formulas of L will be those expressions which we propose later to interpret as making assertions. The sentences will be those among the formulas whose interpretation is independent of the interpretation of the variables.

Among the set F of formulas we recognize as basic the *atomic formulas*, or expressions of the form $rt_1\ldots t_n$, where r is in R_n. We now define the set F of *formulas* to be the smallest set F such that:

(1) every atomic formula is in F;

(2) $\mathsf{0}$ and $\mathsf{1}$ are in F; if p and q are in F, then $\mathsf{N}p$, $\mathsf{C}pq$, and $\mathsf{D}pq$ are in F: if p is in F and x is in V, then $\mathsf{A}xp$ and $\mathsf{E}xp$ are in F.

EXERCISES. Analogs of Exercises 1 through 6 of the section on terms.

The set F of formulas can be made into an algebra of formulas in much the same way as we formed the algebra of terms. The presence of the quantifiers introduces substantial complications, but even ignoring the quantifiers we obtain an algebra of very considerable interest, which we will examine later.

Our present aim is to proceed to the definition of a sentence, and for this we must understand, in syntactical terms, how it is that the interpretation of a formula depends on that of a variable. The formula $x^2 - y^2 = (x + y)(x - y)$, in an elementary textbook, is ordinarily understood as asserting the true identity which we would write as $\mathsf{A}x\mathsf{A}y[x^2 - y^2 = (x + y)(x - y)]$; this makes a statement that is unconditionally true, just as the formula $\mathsf{A}x\mathsf{A}y[x^2 + y^2 = (x + y)^2]$ is unconditionally false. On the other hand, a formula such as $x^2 + 7x + 5 = 0$ cannot be taken, out of context, as making a definite assertion: for some x it is true, for most false. This indefiniteness is clearly due to the occurrence of the variable x without any quantifier or other indication of which values of x are to be considered. Roughly, a sentence will be a formula in which every occurrence of a variable x is governed or bound by a quantifier $\mathsf{A}x$ or $\mathsf{E}x$. We turn now to make this precise.

One expression e may occur as a *part* of another expression $f = aeb$ in more than one place; we shall call a triple (a, e, b) such that $f = aeb$ an *occurrence* of e in f. Given an occurrence (c, f, d) of f in a further expression $g = cfd$, we call the occurrence (ca, e, bd) of e in g a *part* of the given occurrence of f in g.

With this, we define an occurrence of a variable x in an expression e to be *bound* in e if it is part of an occurrence of some formula $\mathsf{A}xp$ or $\mathsf{E}xp$ in e. An occurrence that is not bound is *free*. A *sentence* is a formula that contains no free occurrence of any variable.

We have already indicated that, among formulas, it is only sentences that can be taken as making a definite unambiguous assertion. For most purposes we should prefer to consider only sentences, dispensing entirely with other formulas. However, because a complicated sentence will be built up from components that are not themselves sentences, but only formulas, there seems to be no natural way to define sentences without the intermediary of formulas. This will appear when we want to prove some property P of sentences:

we shall ordinarily have to prove some broader property P' for all formulas, which implies P when restricted to sentences.

INTERPRETATIONS AND STRUCTURES

Roughly speaking, an interpretation ϕ of the language L will assign to the terms t of L certain objects ϕt in a domain A, which the terms may be thought of as naming under the given interpretation. It will assign to each function symbol f of rank n a function ϕf of rank n, from the domain A into itself, and to each relation symbol r of rank n a relation ϕr of rank n on the domain A. A non-empty *domain* A, equipped with functions ϕf indexed by F and relations ϕr indexed by R, will be called a *structure*. This is a modest extension of the concept of an algebra, defined earlier.

We want to think of an interpretation ϕ as attaching to each formula p some assertion about the structure A, which either holds or fails in A. The easiest way out is to take ϕp to be simply the value, truth or falsehood, of this assertion. Since we need not, and would rather not, explain here what is meant by truth and falsehood, we choose instead two neutral objects, the numbers 1 and 0, to serve, respectively, instead of truth and falsehood. We call 0 and 1 the *truth values*, and denote by $\mathsf{B} = \{0, 1\}$ the set of these two truth values. Then, if p is any formula, we shall take ϕp in B. It will be convenient now to require ϕr, for r a relation symbol of rank n, to be not a set of n-tuples, but rather a function of rank n from A into B.

Precisely, an *interpretation* ϕ of L, with *domain* A where A is non-empty, will consist first of all of a function defined on $\mathsf{F} \cup \mathsf{R} \cup T \cup F$, with values as follows:

(i) if f is in F_n, then ϕf is a function from A^n into A;

(ii) if r is in R_n, then ϕr is a function from A^n into B;

(iii) if t is in T, then ϕt is in A;

(iv) if p is in F, then ϕp is in B.

An interpretation is required, further, to satisfy the following conditions:

(1) if f is in F_n and $t_1,\dots,t_n$ are in T, then

$$\phi(ft_1\dots t_n) = (\phi f)(\phi t_1,\dots,\phi t_n);$$

(2) if r is in R_n and $t_1,\dots,t_n$ are in T, then

$$\phi(rt_1\dots t_n) = (\phi r)(\phi t_1,\dots,\phi t_n);$$

(3) $\phi 0 = 0$, $\phi 1 = 1$; and, for p and q in F,

$$\phi(\mathsf{N}p) = 1 - \phi p,\ \phi(\mathsf{C}pq) = \mathrm{Min}(\phi p, \phi q),\ \phi(\mathsf{D}pq) = \mathrm{Max}(\phi p, \phi q);$$

(4) let x be in V and p in F, and define $I(\phi, x)$ to be the set of all interpretations ϕ' that agree with ϕ on $\mathsf{F} \cup \mathsf{R} \cup \mathsf{V}$ except possibly on x: then

$$\phi(\mathsf{A}xp) = 1 \text{ iff } \phi' p = 1 \text{ for all } \phi' \text{ in } I(\phi, x), \text{ and}$$

$$\phi(\mathsf{E}xp) = 1 \text{ iff } \phi' p = 1 \text{ for some } \phi' \text{ in } I(\phi, x).$$

By way of clarification of (3) we remark that $\phi\mathsf{N}p = 1$ iff ϕp is not 1; that $\phi\mathsf{C}pq = 1$ iff $\phi p = 1$ and $\phi q = 1$; and that $\phi\mathsf{D}pq = 1$ iff $\phi p = 1$ or $\phi q = 1$. To clarify (4) we note, in a very informal notation, that $\phi(\mathsf{A}xp(x, y,\dots)) = 1$ should mean $(\phi p)(a, \phi y,\dots)$ for all a in A, that is, taking ϕ' in $I(\phi, x)$ with $\phi' x = a$, that $(\phi' p)(\phi' x, \phi' y,\dots)$, in short, $\phi' p = 1$. The meaning of $\phi(\mathsf{E}xp) = 1$ is explained similarly.

The definition we have given for an interpretation seems to us the most transparent, but it is open to one criticism: clause (4) in the definition of an interpretation refers already to the totality of interpretations. To avoid this appearance of circularity, we give an alternative definition, which is more elegant but more artificial.

For a fixed structure S, that is, for fixed A and ϕ_0 defined on $\mathsf{F} \cup \mathsf{R}$ in accordance with (i) and (ii), let J be the set of all extensions of ϕ_0 to a function ϕ defined on $\mathsf{F} \cup \mathsf{R} \cup T$, and satisfying (iii) and (1). We now define a function assigning to each formula p in F a subset $J(p)$ of J, as follows:

(2′) for $rt_1 \ldots t_n$, an atomic formula, ϕ is in $J(rt_1 \ldots t_n)$ iff $(\phi r)(\phi t_1, \ldots, \phi t_n) = 1$;

(3′) $J(0) = \emptyset$ (empty set), $J(1) = J$, $J(\mathsf{N}p) = J - J(p)$ (complement),
$J(\mathsf{C}pq) = J(p) \cap J(q)$ (intersection), $J(\mathsf{D}pq) = J(p) \cup J(q)$ (union);

(4′) $J(\mathsf{A}xp)$ = set of all ϕ in J such that $J(\phi, x) \subseteq J(p)$, and $J(\mathsf{E}xp)$ = set of all ϕ in J such that $J(\phi, x) \cap J(p) \neq \emptyset$, empty, where $J(\phi, x)$ consists of all ϕ' that agree with ϕ except possibly on x.

We now extend each ϕ in J to a function defined on F as well as on $\mathsf{F} \cup \mathsf{R} \cup T$, by setting $\phi p = 1$ iff ϕ is in $J(p)$. It is easy to see that the functions ϕ in J, thus extended, are precisely the interpretations, in the sense of (i) to (iv) and (1) to (4), with structure S.

EXERCISES

1. If we view the structure S as an algebra with domain A and operations ϕf indexed by F, then (i), (iii), and (1) require that ϕ effect a homomorphism from the algebra T of terms into S. From the fact that T is a free algebra, show that every function ϕ_0 on $\mathsf{V} \cup \mathsf{F}$, with $\phi_0 \mathsf{V} \subseteq A$ and satisfying (i), extends uniquely to a function ϕ on $T \cup \mathsf{F}$ satisfying (i), (iii), and (1).

2. Show that, similarly, every function ϕ_0 defined on the set of atomic formulas and with values in B extends uniquely to a function ϕ on the set of formulas that contains no quantifiers, and satisfying (3).

3. Show that every function ϕ_0 defined on $\mathsf{V} \cup \mathsf{F} \cup \mathsf{R}$, and taking values in accordance with (i), (ii), and (iii), extends uniquely to an interpretation.

In view of Exercise 3, we shall often speak of an interpretation ϕ simply as a function defined on $\mathsf{V} \cup \mathsf{F} \cup \mathsf{R}$, the extension to $T \cup F$ being understood. The structure of the interpretation can then be identified with the restriction of ϕ to $\mathsf{F} \cup \mathsf{R}$.

DEPENDENCE AND SUBSTITUTION

It should be obvious that the value ϕt of a term t under an interpretation ϕ depends only upon the values ϕs that ϕ attaches to those symbols that occur in t. Nonetheless, we give this a formal statement and proof.

> PROPOSITION. Let t be a term, and ϕ and ϕ' two interpretations that agree on every symbol that occurs in t. Then $\phi t = \phi' t$.

To prove this we let U be the set of all terms for which the assertion of the proposition holds; since $U \subseteq T$, it will do to show that $T \subseteq U$. Referring to the definition of the set T of terms, we note first that $\mathsf{V} \subseteq U$, and it remains only, assuming f in F_n and $t_1, \ldots, t_n$ in U, to show that $t = ft_1 \ldots t_n$ is in U. If ϕ and ϕ' agree on every symbol in t, then surely $\phi f = \phi' f$ and also ϕ and ϕ' agree on every symbol in $t_1, \ldots, t_n$. Since $t_1, \ldots, t_n$ are in U, we have $\phi t_1 = \phi' t_1, \ldots, \phi t_n = \phi' t_n$. From (2) in the definition of an interpretation, we have that

$$\phi(ft_1 \ldots t_n) = (\phi f)(\phi t_1, \ldots, \phi t_n)$$

and

$$\phi'(ft_1 \ldots t_n) = (\phi' f)(\phi' t_1, \ldots, \phi' t_n),$$

whence

$$\phi t = \phi' t.$$

The analogous result for formulas runs as follows.

> PROPOSITION. Let p be a formula, and ϕ and ϕ' two interpretations that agree on every symbol that occurs in p,

except possibly variables that do not occur free in p. Then $\phi p = \phi' p$.

To prove this, let U be the set of all formulas for which the assertion holds. The proof that every atomic formula is in U, and that 0, 1, Np, Cpq, and Dpq are in U provided p and q are, presents nothing new. It remains to show that if p is in U, then Axp and Exp are in U; we treat Exp, the other case being entirely similar. By symmetry, it will do to show that $\phi \mathrm{E}xp = 1$ implies $\phi' \mathrm{E}xp = 1$. Now $\phi \mathrm{E}xp = 1$ implies that $\psi p = 1$ for some ψ that differs from ϕ (on the set V ∪ F ∪ R) at most at x. We construct ψ' to differ from ϕ' at most at x, where we take $\psi' x = \psi x$, which is possible by virtue of an Exercise. Then ψ and ψ' agree on all f in F and r in R that occur in p, and on all v in V that occur free in Exp, and also on x. Thus ψ and ψ' satisfy the hypothesis with respect to p, and $\psi p = \psi' p$. Hence $\psi' p = 1$, and $\phi' \mathrm{E}xp = 1$.

The concept of substitution, at its simplest, is exemplified by the following refinement of the first proposition; the proof is easy and is left as an Exercise.

PROPOSITION. Let t and u be terms and x a variable, and let t' be the term obtained by replacing x by u at every occurrence in t. If ϕ and ϕ' are two interpretations, agreeing on all symbols except possibly x that occur in t, and such that $\phi x = \phi' u$, then $\phi t = \phi' t'$.

In the situation described, we write $t = t(x)$ and $t' = t(u)$ with the obvious meaning.

For formulas, the situation is somewhat more complicated; if $f(x) = \int_1^x xy\,dy$, the formula $f(y) = \int_1^y y^2 dy$ obtained by replacing x (at all free occurrences) by y does not define the same function. We are interested in the result p', of substituting u for x at all free occurrences of x in a formula p, only under the assumption that no occurrence of u thus introduced contains a bound occurrence of a variable. In this case we write $p = p(x)$ and $p' = p(u)$, and the use of this notation is always to be taken as tacitly assuming this hypothesis. [Thus, substitution, in the present restricted sense, of u

for x in p, cannot always be carried out.]

PROPOSITION. If ϕ and ϕ' are two interpretations that agree on all symbols from $F \cup R$ that occur in $p(x)$, and on all variables that occur free in $p(x)$ except possibly on x, and if $\phi x = \phi' u$, then $\phi p(x) = \phi' p(u)$.

For the proof, it will do to treat the case that $p(x)$ has the form $\mathrm{E}yq$. If $x = y$, then x does not occur free in $p(x)$, whence $p(x) = p(u)$, and the conclusion follows from an earlier proposition. Assuming that $x \neq y$, we have $p(x) = \mathrm{E}yq(x)$ and $p(u) = \mathrm{E}yq(u)$, with the hypothesis that y does not occur in u. We match the ψ agreeing with ϕ except possibly on y with the ψ' agreeing with ϕ' except possibly on y by the condition $\psi y = \psi' y$. Since y does not occur in u, we have $\psi' u = \phi' u$, and hence $\psi x = \phi x = \phi' u = \psi' u$. The induction hypothesis now gives $\psi q(x) = \psi' q(u)$, whence the existence of ψ such that $\psi q(x) = 1$ is equivalent to that of ψ' such that $\psi' q(u) = 1$, and the conditions $\phi \mathrm{E}yq(x) = 1$ and $\phi' \mathrm{E}yq(u) = 1$ are equivalent.

We note an important consequence of the second proposition.

COROLLARY. If p is a sentence, then ϕp has the same value for all interpretations ϕ in the same structure; that is, ϕp depends only on the values of ϕ on $F \cup R$ and not upon its values on V.

SEMANTIC IMPLICATION

We define the relation of *semantic implication*, $p \models q$, between two formulas of L, to hold iff, for every interpretation ϕ, $\phi p = 1$ implies $\phi q = 1$. For sets of formulas, $P \models Q$ means similarly that $\phi P = 1$ implies $\phi Q = 1$ for all ϕ.

If $p \models q$ and $q \models p$, we write $p \models\!\mid q$ and call p and q *semantically equivalent*.

If $\emptyset \models q$, that is, if $\phi q = 1$ for every interpretation ϕ, we write $\models q$ and say that q is *valid* or (universally) *true*.

If $P \models 0$, that is, if $\phi P = 1$ for no interpretation ϕ, we say that P is *semantically inconsistent*, and otherwise that P is *semantically consistent*. If $\phi P = 1$, it is customary to say that the interpretation ϕ, or sometimes the associated structure, is a *model* for P. By definition, then, a set P of formulas is semantically consistent iff it possesses a model.

We introduce the notation J as an abbreviation for the expression DN, whence, for all formulas p and q, $\mathsf{J}pq = \mathsf{DN}pq$; we shall also use the more common notation $p \supset q$ for $\mathsf{J}pq$. Notice that $\phi\mathsf{J}pq = 1$ except in the case that $\phi p = 1$ and yet $\phi q = 0$. Thus the syntactical operation J on a pair of formulas expresses the relation of semantic implication in the following sense.

PROPOSITION. For formulas p and q, $\models p \supset q$ iff $p \models q$.

It is important to notice that the symbol $\models$ denotes a relation between formulas, analogous to the relation $x \geq y$ between numbers, whereas the symbol J denotes an operation on formulas, to form a composite formula, analogous to the operation of forming the difference $x - y$ of two numbers. The proposition is then analogous to the fact that $x - y \geq 0$ iff $x \geq y$. In particular, it is important to recognize that the proposition $p \supset q$ falls far short of providing us with a syntactically defined equivalent of the semantic relation $p \models q$.

If we are considering a theory T defined semantically by reference to a specified class I_0 of interpretations, we shall in principle write $P \models_{I_0} Q$ iff $\phi P = 1$ implies $\phi Q = 1$ for all ϕ in I_0, and we attach a subscript I_0 to the other related concepts. In practice, we shall commonly omit the subscript.

SENTENTIAL LOGIC

We have now set up all the necessary machinery, but we shall employ it first in a somewhat simplified situation, that is, with the symbols A and E deleted from our language L. In this case little is lost by deleting also the variables, the function symbols, and all the relation symbols of rank greater than 0. The resulting language L will be called a *sentential language*. Such languages are of great interest in their own right, and they provide also a simple introduction to the study of more general languages, although one should be warned that the results for sentential languages are far simpler, and in some cases in direct contrast, to those for more general languages.

We recapitulate our definitions, for L now a sentential language. The *symbols* of L are the five *connectives* O, 1, N, C, and D, together with a set R_0 of *relation symbols*, all now of rank 0. There are no terms. The *atomic formulas* are precisely the elements of R_0. The set F of *formulas* is the smallest such that $R_0 \subseteq F$, that O and 1 are in F, and that Np, Cpq, and Dpq are in F whenever p and q are in F. The *sentences* are exactly the formulas.

Since there are no terms, the domain of an interpretation becomes irrelevant, and the concept of an *interpretation* and *structure* coincide, reducing to that of a function ϕ from R_0 into B subject to the following conditions:

$$\phi \mathrm{O} = 0,\ \phi 1 = 1,\ \phi \mathrm{N}p = 1 - \phi p,$$

$$\phi \mathrm{C}pq = \mathrm{Min}(\phi p, \phi q),\ \phi \mathrm{D}pq = \mathrm{Max}(\phi p, \phi q).$$

The definitions of semantic implication and validity are unchanged.

The problem of giving a syntactical characterization of the relation $p \models q$ of semantic implication turns out to have an easy solution for sentential languages. First, from the fact that $p \models q$ iff $\models Jpq$, it follows that it will do to characterize the valid formulas. Let p be any formula, and $r_1,\ldots,r_n$ the finite set of relation symbols that occur in p. Since the value ϕp depends only on the n values $\phi r_1,\ldots,\phi r_n$, p will be valid iff $\phi_i p = 1$ for each of 2^n interpretations ϕ_i assigning to $r_1,\ldots,r_n$ the values 0 and 1 in every combination. For each ϕ_i, let $\phi_i^* p$ be the formula obtained from p by replacing each r_j by 0 if $\phi_i r_j = 0$, and by 1 if $\phi_i r_j = 1$. It is easy to show that ϕ_i assigns the same value to p and $\phi_i^* p$. Thus our problem reduces to that of deciding whether ϕ_i assigns the value 1 to $\phi_i^* p$. Since the $\phi_i^* p$ contain no relation symbols, we need only decide the validity of formulas q containing no relation symbols. The question of validity for such a formula q can be reduced to that for an equivalent shorter formula q' obtained by a replacement of one of the following sorts:

N0 by 1; N1 by 0; C00, C01, C10 by 0 and C11 by 1;

D00 by 0, and D01, D10, D11 by 1;

until q is found to be equivalent to either 0 or 1. Evidently, q is valid iff q is equivalent to 1.

Clearly the above argument provides a process, which can be carried out entirely within the syntax of L and without mention of validity or equivalence, for deciding whether given p is valid. Under any reasonable sense of the word decidable we have proved then the following theorem.

THEOREM. It is decidable whether an arbitrary formula of a sentenial language is valid.

THE ALGEBRA OF PROPOSITIONS

We now make the set F of formulas into an algebra, the *algebra of formulas*, with two operations of rank 0, or constants, one operation of rank 1, and two of rank 2. The operations, 0, 1, $\neg$, $\wedge$, and $\vee$, are defined as follows:

$$0 = 0, \quad 1 = 1, \quad \neg p = Np, \quad p \wedge q = Cpq, \quad p \vee q = Dpq.$$

We make the set B of truth values into an *algebra of truth values*, with operations denoted by the same symbols, by taking 0 and 1 as given and defining

$$\neg x = 1 - x, \quad x \wedge y = \mathrm{Min}(x,y), \quad x \vee y = \mathrm{Max}(x,y).$$

An interpretation ϕ then becomes simply a homomorphism from F into B. These simple observations enable us to apply standard algebraic procedures to the study of L.

If ϕ is any map from a set A into a set A', the *kernel* of ϕ is the binary relation $x \equiv y$ defined on A by the condition $\phi x = \phi y$. A binary relation is an (abstract) *equivalence relation* if it is:

reflexive:	$x \equiv x$	for all x;
symmetric:	$x \equiv y$	implies $y \equiv x$, for all x and y;
transitive:	$x \equiv y$	and $y \equiv z$ implies $x \equiv z$, for all x, y, and z.

The kernel of any map from A into A' is an equivalence relation. If an equivalence relation $x \equiv y$ is given on a set A, we define the *coset* $[x]$ of an element x in A to consist of all y such that $x \equiv y$, and we write $[A]$ for the collection of all such cosets. A family P of non-empty subsets of a set A is a *partition* if each element of A belongs to exactly one member of P. If $x \equiv y$ is an equivalence relation on A, then $[A]$ is a partition of A. If a partition P of A is given, the *canonical map* κ from A onto P assigns to each x in A the unique element $\kappa(x)$ of P containing x; then P is the partition derived from the kernel of κ. If ϕ from A into A' is given, and $[A]$ is the partition derived from the kernel of ϕ, then there is a unique one to one function ϕ' from $[A]$ into A' such that, for all x, $\phi x = \phi'[x]$.

If a family of equivalence relations on A, $x \equiv_i y$, is given for i in an index set I, then their *intersection*, $x \equiv y$, defined to hold iff $x \equiv_i y$ for all i in I, is also an equivalence relation.

If A and A' are algebras and ϕ a homomorphism, the kernel is a *congruence*, that is, an equivalence that is substitutive in all the operations of A: if w is an operation of rank n, then, for all $x_1, \ldots, x_n$ and $y_1, \ldots, y_n$ in A, one has that

$$x_1 \equiv y_1 \text{ and } \ldots \text{ and } x_n \equiv y_n \text{ implies } w(x_1, \ldots, x_n) \equiv w(y_1, \ldots, y_n).$$

If $[A]$ is the partition of A derived from a congruence, then we can make $[A]$ into an algebra, the *quotient algebra* of A by $\equiv$, by defining operations w on $[A]$ that satisfy the conditions

$$w([x_1], \ldots, [x_n]) = [w(x_1, \ldots, x_n)] \text{ for all } x_1, \ldots, x_n \text{ in } A.$$

With these modifications, all the results stated above for equivalence relations carry over to congruences.

To apply this to the algebra of formulas, we observe that the relation $p \models\!\dashv q$ on F is the intersection of all the congruences $\phi p = \phi q$ associated with interpretations ϕ, and hence is itself a congruence. The quotient algebra $[F]$ of F by the relation $p \models\!\dashv q$ is called the *Lindenbaum algebra* of L.

As far as semantics is concerned, there is little interest in distinguishing between synonymous formulas, which take the same value under each interpretation. If we lump together with p all formulas semantically equivalent with p, we obtain the element $[p]$ of the Lindenbaum algebra. There is some justification for viewing $[p]$ as the common meaning of these various formulas, and calling $[p]$ a *proposition* and the Lindenbaum algebra $[F]$ also the *algebra of propositions* of L. To illustrate this, note that, unless $p = q$, the two formulas $p \wedge q$ and $q \wedge p$ of F are distinct, although they have the same meaning: $p \wedge q \models\!\dashv q \wedge p$. It follows that $[p] \wedge [q]$ and $[q] \wedge [p]$ are the same element of $[F]$, and in the algebra of propositions we have the law that $x \wedge y = y \wedge x$ for all x and y in $[F]$.

DISJUNCTIVE FORM

The algebra of propositions, $[F]$, displays a certain analogy to ordinary algebra, with $\wedge$ in the role of multiplication and $\vee$ in that of addition. Thus the law $x \wedge y = y \wedge x$ is the analog of the law $xy = yx$ in ordinary algebra. In ordinary algebra the value of a product does not depend on the order of the factors or the arrangement of parentheses, and we employ the notation $p = \Pi_1^n x_i$ for the product of n factors $x_1, \ldots, x_n$. In the algebra of propositions, an element p built up by means of the operation $\wedge$ alone from elements $x_1, \ldots, x_n$ does not depend on order or grouping, nor does it depend on the frequency of occurence of the x_i, provided only that each occurs at least once. We write $p = \bigwedge_1^n x_i$ for the conjunction of $x_1, \ldots, x_n$; as in ordinary algebra, if $n = 0$, we take this to mean that $p = 1$. By analogy with the ordinary notation $p = \Sigma_1^n x_i$, we introduce the notation $p = \bigvee_1^n x_i$ for the disjunction of elements $x_1, \ldots, x_n$, that is, for any element p built up by the operation $\vee$ alone from the x_i, and containing each x_i at least once. If $n = 0$, we take $p = \bigvee_1^n x_i$ to mean that $p = 0$.

In ordinary algebra a polynomial is, apart from its coefficients, a sum of products. Here we define a *polynomial* in $x_1, \ldots, x_n$ to be a disjunction of conjunctions of the x_i and their negations $\neg x_i$, that is, an element of the form $p = \bigvee_i \bigwedge_j s_{ij}$, where each s_{ij} is some x_k or $\neg x_k$. We shall show that every element of $[F]$, built up by means of the operations of $[F]$ from elements $x_1, \ldots, x_n$, can be expressed as a polynomial in $x_1, \ldots, x_n$, and that, under suitable restrictions, this expression is unique.

In our discussion we have spoken not only of elements of $[F]$ but also, somewhat vaguely, of expressions for elements of $[F]$. To clarify this, it is both natural and convenient to pass to F, whose elements are indeed expressions for the elements of $[F]$. We turn to the precise statement and proof of our assertions in these terms.

A formula p of F is in *disjunctive form* if:

(1) no subformula of p that begins with N contains another occurrence of N, or an occurence of 0, 1, C, or D;

(2) no subformula of p that begins with C contains 0, 1, or D;

(3) no subformula of p that begins with D contains 0 or 1.

PROPOSITION. Every formula is equivalent to a formula in disjunctive form.

We show first that every formula p is equivalent to 0 or 1 or to a formula that does not contain 0 or 1. If p contains 0 or 1, then by the rules

$$\mathrm{N0} \models\!\mid 1, \quad \mathrm{C0}x \models\!\mid \mathrm{C}x0 \models\!\mid 0, \quad \mathrm{D0}x \models\!\mid \mathrm{D}x0 \models\!\mid x,$$

$$\mathrm{N1} \models\!\mid 0, \quad \mathrm{C1}x \models\!\mid \mathrm{C}x1 \models\!\mid x, \quad \mathrm{D1}x \models\!\mid \mathrm{D}x1 \models\!\mid 1,$$

together with the substitutivity of $x \models\!\mid y$, we can replace p by a shorter equivalent formula. Continuing thus, we ultimately arrive at some p' equivalent to p which either is 0 or 1, or does not contain 0 or 1.

Next supposing p does not contain 0 or 1, we show that p is equivalent to a formula that does not contain 0 or 1, and which has no part NN, NC or ND. Indeed, if p contains such a part, then by one of the rules

$$\mathrm{NN}x \models\!\mid x, \quad \mathrm{NC}xy \models\!\mid \mathrm{DN}x\mathrm{N}y, \quad \mathrm{ND}xy \models\!\mid \mathrm{CN}x\mathrm{N}y,$$

we can replace p by equivalent p' in such a way that the number of occurrences of N, C, and D other than initially in a subformula beginning with N is diminished. Ultimately we arrive at some p' in which N occurs only in subformulas Nr where r is atomic.

Finally, supposing p contains no part 0, 1, NN, NC or ND, we show that p is equivalent to a formula with the same property and such that no subformula beginning with C contains D. Indeed, by the rules

$$\mathrm{CD}xyz \mathrel{\models\!\!\!\dashv} \mathrm{DC}xz\mathrm{C}yz, \qquad \mathrm{C}x\mathrm{D}yz \mathrel{\models\!\!\!\dashv} \mathrm{DC}xy\mathrm{C}xz,$$

we can diminish the number of occurrences of D in subformulas beginning with C until such a formula p' is reached. Clearly p' is now in disjunctive form.

A formula p is in *reduced disjunctive form* if it is in disjunctive form and, moreover,

(4) a subformula of p that begins with C contains no atomic formula more than once.

PROPOSITION. Every formula is equivalent to a formula in reduced disjunctive form.

If q is a subformula of p that begins with C, and hence is built up by C alone from subformulas r_i and Nr_i for r_i atomic, then, by the rules

$$\mathrm{C}xy \mathrel{\models\!\!\!\dashv} \mathrm{C}yx, \qquad \mathrm{C}x\mathrm{C}yz \mathrel{\models\!\!\!\dashv} \mathrm{CC}xyz,$$

we can permute the subformulas r_i and Nr_i at will. If q contains two occurrences of some atomic formula r, then we can suppose that q contains a part of one of the forms Crr, CrNr, CNrr, CNrNr. By one of the rules,

$$\mathrm{C}xx \mathrel{\models\!\!\!\dashv} x, \qquad \mathrm{C}x\mathrm{N}x \mathrel{\models\!\!\!\dashv} \mathrm{CN}xx \mathrel{\models\!\!\!\dashv} 0,$$

we can replace this part by an equivalent part r, Nr, or 0. Since this yields a formula p' equivalent to p and shorter than p, the proposition follows by induction.

A formula p is in *complete disjunctive form* with respect to an ordered set $r_1, \ldots, r_n$ of distinct atomic formulas, if it has the following form. If $n = 0$, then $p = 0$ or $p = 1$. If $n > 0$, then either $p = 0$ or, for some $m \geq 1$, p has the form $p = \mathsf{D}q_1\mathsf{D}q_2 \ldots \mathsf{D}q_{m-2}\mathsf{D}q_{m-1}q_m$, where each q_i, in turn, has the form $q_i = \mathsf{C}s_{i1}\mathsf{C}s_{i2} \ldots \mathsf{C}s_{in-2}\mathsf{C}s_{in-1}s_{in}$ and each s_{ij} is r_i or $\mathsf{N}r_i$. Moreover, if $1 \leq i < h \leq m$, then there exists some k, $1 \leq k \leq n$, such that $s_{i1} = s_{h1}, \ldots, s_{ik-1} = s_{hk-1}$ while $s_{ik} = r_i$ and $s_{hk} = \mathsf{N}r_i$.

PROPOSITION. If a formula p contains no atomic formulas other than $r_1, \ldots, r_n$, then p is equivalent to a formula in complete disjunctive form with respect to $r_1, \ldots, r_n$.

We can suppose that p, in disjunctive form, is built up by D alone from parts q_i that do not contain D. By the rules

$$\mathsf{D}x\mathsf{N}x \models\!\dashv 1, \qquad \mathsf{C}x1 \models\!\dashv x, \qquad \mathsf{C}x\mathsf{D}yz \models\!\dashv \mathsf{D}\mathsf{C}xy\mathsf{C}xz,$$

we can replace q_i by $\mathsf{D}\mathsf{C}q_ir_j\mathsf{C}q_i\mathsf{N}r_j$; that is, we can replace q_i by the two parts $q_i' = \mathsf{C}q_ir_j$ and $q_i'' = \mathsf{C}q_i\mathsf{N}r_j$. In this way we can ensure that each q_i contains each r_j. As before, we can arrange that each q_i contains the $r_1, \ldots, r_n$ in order, and none more than once. Thus the q_i have the required form.

By the rules

$$\mathsf{D}xx \models\!\dashv x, \qquad \mathsf{D}xy \models\!\dashv \mathsf{D}yx, \qquad \mathsf{D}x\mathsf{D}yz \models\!\dashv \mathsf{D}\mathsf{D}xyz,$$

we can similarly rearrange the occurrences of the q_i in p so that they occur in the prescribed lexicographical order, with the prescribed grouping, and with none occurring more than once. Then p is in complete disjunctive form.

PROPOSITION. If p is in reduced disjunctive form, then $p \models\!\dashv 0$ iff $p = 0$.

Assuming $p \neq 0$ we must show that, for some interpretation ϕ, $\phi p = 1$. If $p = 1$, any ϕ will do. Otherwise p is a disjunction of parts q_i containing only the connectives C and N, and it will suffice to find ϕ such that some $\phi q_i = 1$. Now q_i is built up from certain r_j and Nr_j by means of C alone, and contains no r_j twice. Let J be the set of j such that q_i contains Nr_j. Since the atomic formulas constitute a basis for the algebra F of formulas, the map ϕ from R_0 into B defined by setting $\phi r_j = 0$ for j in J and $\phi r_j = 1$ for j not in J can be extended to an interpretation ϕ. Since q_i is built up by C alone from parts Nr_j with j in J and parts r_h for h not in J, and since $\phi Nr_j = 1$ and $\phi r_h = 1$ for such parts, it follows that $\phi q_i = 1$, as required.

> PROPOSITION. If p and p' are in complete disjunctive form with respect to $r_1, \ldots, r_n$, then $p \models\!\!\!\!\dashv p'$ iff $p = p'$.

This is trivial if $n = 0$. Otherwise, assuming $p \neq p'$, the set of q_i occurring in p is not the same as that occurring in p', and we may suppose, by symmetry, that some q_i occurs in p but not in p'. If we construct ϕ as before, then $\phi q_i = 1$ and hence $\phi p = 1$. If some q_h occurs in p', then $q_h \neq q_i$ by assumption, and, for some k, one of s_{ik}, s_{hk} is r_k and the other is Nr_k. Since $\phi s_{ik} = 1$, it follows that $\phi s_{hk} = 0$, and, since q_h is built up from the s_{hj} by C alone, it follows that $\phi q_h = 0$. Finally, since p' is built up by D alone from various q_h such that $\phi q_h = 0$, it follows that $\phi p' = 0$.

BOOLEAN ALGEBRA

We shall examine more closely the algebraic structure of the algebra $[F]$ of propositions. We have noticed that $[F]$ satisfies the law $x \wedge y = y \wedge x$, and, in the preceding section, we listed a fair number of other laws that hold in $[F]$. One may hope to describe $[F]$ by specifying all the laws that hold in $[F]$. There is an easy answer to this problem: the set of laws that hold in $[F]$ is precisely the set of all laws that hold in B. This follows from the definition of $[F]$ in terms of the set of all homomorphisms from F into B.

EXERCISE. Prove this.

An algebra that satisfies all these laws is called a *Boolean algebra*. A Boolean algebra A is a *free Boolean algebra* with *basis* B if B is a subset of A such that every map from B into a Boolean algebra A' has a unique extension to a homomorphism from A into A'. Now $[F]$ is a free Boolean algebra with basis R_0, and B is a free Boolean algebra with the empty set as basis.

EXERCISE. Prove these assertions.

There is a second related and equally important source of Boolean algebras. Let E be any set, and A the family of all subsets x of E. We make A into an algebra by taking 0 to be the empty set, 1 to be the full set E, and, for x and y in A, taking $\neg x$ to be the complement $E - x$ of x, $x \wedge y$ to be the intersection $x \cap y$, and $x \vee y$ to be the union $x \cup y$. Then A is the *algebra of all subsets* of E. If A' is any subcollection of A that is *closed* under the operations: $0, 1$ are in A' and, for x and y in A', also $\neg x$, $x \wedge y$, and $x \vee y$ are in A', then A' is also an algebra under the same operations restricted to A'. We call A' simply an *algebra of subsets* of E.

PROPOSITION. Any algebra of subsets of a set is a Boolean algebra.

It will do to prove this for the algebra A of all subsets of a set E. For each element e in E, we define a map ϕ_e from A into B by setting $\phi_e x = 1$ iff e is in x. It is easy to see that each ϕ_e is a homomorphism, and that $x = y$ iff $\phi_e x = \phi_e y$ for all e in E. Suppose that a law $H(a_1, \ldots, a_n) = K(a_1, \ldots, a_n)$ holds in B. If $x_1, \ldots, x_n$ are elements of A, then, for each e in E, $\phi_e H(x_1, \ldots, x_n) = H(\phi_e x_1, \ldots, \phi_e x_n) = K(\phi_e x_1, \ldots, \phi_e x_n) = \phi_e K(x_1, \ldots, x_n)$, whence $H(x_1, \ldots, x_n) = K(x_1, \ldots, x_n)$. Thus the law holds in A.

PROPOSITION. The algebra $[F]$ of propositions is isomorphic to an algebra of sets.

Let E be the set of all homomorphisms from F into $\mathbb{B}$. To each element $[p]$ of $[F]$ we may associate the set $J[p]$ of all those homomorphisms ϕ such that $\phi p = 1$. The routine observations that J is a homomorphism was noted in connection with the definition of an interpretation. That J is one to one, that is, that $J[p] = J[q]$ implies $p = q$, is the condition by which we defined $[F]$ as a quotient algebra of F.

The class of all Boolean algebras can be described more explicitly as that of all algebras satisfying a certain finite set of laws.

PROPOSITION. An algebra A, with operations $0, 1, \neg x$, $x \wedge y$, $x \vee y$, is a Boolean algebra if it satisfies all the following laws:

$$\neg 0 = 1,\ 0 \wedge x = 0,\ 0 \vee x = x,\ \neg 1 = 0,\ 1 \wedge x = x,\ 1 \vee x = 1,$$

$$\neg\neg x = x,\ \neg(x \wedge y) = \neg x \vee \neg y,\ \neg(x \vee y) = \neg x \wedge \neg y,$$

$$(x \wedge y) \vee z = (x \vee z) \wedge (y \vee z),\ (x \vee y) \wedge z = (x \wedge z) \vee (y \wedge z),$$

$$x \wedge x = x,\ x \wedge y = y \wedge x,\ (x \wedge y) \wedge z = x \wedge (y \wedge z),$$

$$x \vee x = x,\ x \vee y = y \vee x,\ (x \vee y) \vee z = x \vee (y \vee z),$$

$$x \wedge \neg x = 0,\ x \vee \neg x = 1.$$

First, it is routine to check that all these laws hold in the two element algebra $\mathbb{B}$, and hence in every Boolean algebra. Next, define a relation $p \equiv q$ on F to hold iff the equation $p = q$ is a consequence of imposing all the above laws on F. It will suffice to show that, if $p \models\!\dashv q$, then $p \equiv q$. Now, the laws above are, apart from minor rearrangements, exactly the laws that were used in transforming arbitrary p into equivalent complete disjunctive form. If p and q are two formulas containing no relation symbols except $r_1, \ldots, r_n$, and p' and q' are their complete disjunctive forms with respect to these symbols, then $p \equiv p'$ and $q \equiv q'$. Suppose now that $p \models\!\dashv q$; then, it was shown, $p' = q'$. Since the relation $\equiv$ is clearly an equivalence, it follows that $p \equiv q$.

EXERCISES

1. The set of laws given above is highly redundant; simplify it.

2. Every Boolean algebra A is in fact isomorphic to an algebra of subsets of the set $J(A)$ of its homomorphisms into $\mathbb{B}$ [Stone's Theorem]. For finite A prove this, and show that A is free.

3. If A is finite it is isomorphic to the algebra of all subsets of $J(A)$, whereas if A is infinite this need not be the case. Prove these two assertions. Hint: an algebra of all subsets of a non-empty set has minimal elements or *atoms* x with the property that, for all y, either $x \wedge y = x$ or $x \wedge y = 0$; show that a free algebra with infinite basis has no atoms.

The discussion of the Lindenbaum algebra remains valid for L not restricted to be a sentential language, but the analysis of $[F]$ as a Boolean algebra fails to give an adequate account of $[F]$, since it ignores the role of the variables and quantifiers. To remedy this defect, two rather similar generalizations of Boolean algebra have been defined: the *cylindric algebras* of Tarski and his collaborators, and the *polyadic algebras* of Halmos. Both have an infinite number of cylindrification operators C_x with the interpretation that $C_x[p] = [\exists xp]$. The polyadic algebras possess substitution operators which replace the variables by one another; in the cylindric algebras, with hyperplanes $[x=y]$, this is accomplished by the observation that $[\exists x(p(x) \wedge x = y)] = [p(y)]$.

EXERCISE. We may view $[p(x, y, z)]$ as the locus in space of points (x, y, z) satisfying $p(x, y, z)$; show that $C_z[p(x, y, z)]$ is the vertical cylinder generated by $[p(x, y, z)]$.

VARIANTS OF SENTENTIAL LOGIC

A number of variants of the usual, or *classical, logic* have been introduced. Some have been developed out of curiosity or the desire to see the classical theory in better perspective, but most represent attempts to remedy some inadequacy of classical logic. They are not usually restricted to sentential logic, and we impose this limitation here only for simplicity.

Other two-valued logics. Classical logic is two-valued in the sense that the set B of truth values has two elements. The nature of the two elements is immaterial, but one may modify sentential logic by taking connectives corresponding to some set of operations other than the set $0, 1, \rightharpoondown x, x \wedge y,$ and $x \vee y$. In one sense, nothing can be gained in this way, for the set listed is *functionally complete*: every operation on B of finite rank is expressible in terms of these five. One cannot increase the expressive power of L, although one may improve the formalism. It is of course possible to decrease the expressive power of L, and it is of some interest to see what can be accomplished with more limited means: for example, the theory with single connective J is of some importance.

EXERCISES

1. Prove functional completeness of the classical sentential calculus. Hint: Use the complete disjunctive form.

2. Show that $0, 1, +,$ and $\times$ form a functionally complete set, where operations are modulo 2, that is, with $1 + 1 = 0$.

3. Show that the set consisting solely of Sheffer's connective, $\mathsf{S}pq = \mathsf{CN}p\mathsf{N}q$, is functionally complete.

4. Show that J alone is not complete; examine the resulting logic.

Many-valued logics. For the commonest of these, B is replaced by some set C of real numbers x, $0 \leq x \leq 1$, for which the definitions of the operations may be carried over without change. It has been suggested that truth values between 0 and 1 correspond to various degrees of uncertainty, but the fact that, for example, if $\phi p = 1/2$ then $\phi(p \vee \neg p) = 1/2$, does not entirely fit this suggestion.

EXERCISES

1. Which laws of Boolean algebra remain true if B is replaced by $C = \{0, 1/2, 1\}$?

2. Are the five operations a complete set on this C?

3. Are the many-valued logics described above decidable?

Probability theory. Probability theory, in its most primitive form, resembles many-valued logic in that it attaches to each formula p as probability a number $Pr(p)$ in the interval $0 \leq x \leq 1$. One common way to do this is to suppose an area or measure attached to every subset of the set J of all interpretations or events, and to take for $Pr(p)$ the area of the set $J(p)$ of all interpretations ϕ such that $\phi p = 1$. Now probability, as an area function, satisfies the formula $Pr(p \vee q) = Pr(p) = + Pr(q) - Pr(p \wedge q)$. Thus probability differs from logic in the present sense in that $Pr(p \vee q)$ does not depend only upon $Pr(p)$ and $Pr(q)$.

Modal logic. Modal logics attempt to incorporate modalities such as necessity and possibility into sentential logic. Commonly a connective $\blacksquare$ is introduced, with $\blacksquare p$ to mean that p is necessarily true; then $\blacklozenge p = \neg \blacksquare \neg p$ means the possibility of p, and the connective $p \prec q = \blacksquare(p \supset q)$ expresses what has been called strict implication. Strict implication was introduced by Lewis to remedy the defect of the connective $p \supset q$, or material implication, that it sometimes holds accidentally: for example, (ice is hot) $\supset$ (grass is green). Kripke has provided recently a suggestive semantics for modal logic, roughly as follows. With each interpretation ϕ in the usual sense is associated a set $K(\phi)$ of other interpretations ϕ with the same domain; these are possible worlds to ϕ's real world. The meaning of

$\blacksquare$ is fixed by taking $\phi(\blacksquare p) = 1$ iff $\phi p = 1$ for all ϕ in $K(\phi)$. The formal analogy with the condition for $\phi(\mathsf{A}xp) = 1$ is evident; here the function and relation symbols are in some sense universally quantified.

Intuitionistic logic. Intuitionistic logic is the most important among the variants of classical logic. Intuitionism is a well-developed philosophical position which expresses serious criticism of the methods of reasoning in classical mathematics, and proposes that mathematical reasoning, especially concerning infinite sets, be restricted to certain constructive and intuitively immediate principles. As a very rough example, a sentence $\mathsf{E}xp(x)$, about natural numbers, can be interpreted as asserting that there exists a natural number n which can be found and shown to have the property p. Its formal negation, $\mathsf{A}x \neg p(x)$, can be understood constructively only as asserting that there is a means of showing, for each n, that n does not have the property p. But now it is entirely conceivable that neither sentence be true in this constructive sense. On such grounds, intuitionists do not accept the universal validity of the formula $p \vee \neg p$ expressing the *Law of Excluded Middle.* Heyting has axiomatized the intuitionistic sentential calculus; there is one such axiomatization that differs only in the omission of the Law of Excluded Middle from a natural axiomatization of the classical sentential logic.

We shall not discuss the syntax and deductive theory of intuitionistic logic here, but will describe Tarski's semantic definition of validity for intuitionistic sentential logic. The language L is the same as in the classical theory, but, for the semantics, we replace B by C, a family of subsets of some topological space E. For simplicity we take E to be the plane.

Let U be a subset of E. We define the *interior* U^* of U to consist of all points x of E such that U contains the whole of some circular region of positive radius and center at x. A set U is *open* if $U = U^*$. We now define C to be the set of all open subsets of E.

The empty set $0 = \emptyset$ and the whole plane $1 = E$ are open sets. Moreover, if U and V are open sets, then $U \cap V$ and $U \cup V$ are open, whence we may define $U \wedge V = U \cap V$ and $U \vee V = U \cup V$.

If U is open, the complementary set $E - U$ need not be open; we define $\neg U$ to be $(E - U)^*$, the largest open set disjoint from U. This last ensures that $U \wedge \neg U = 0$, a law which, unlike the Law of Excluded Middle, we do not want to discard. To show that the Law of Excluded Middle fails, let U be the open lower half plane: $U = [(x, y)\colon\ y < 0]$. Then $E - U$ is the closed upper half plane, $E - U = [(x, y)\colon\ y \geq 0]$, whence $\neg U = (E - U)^*$ is the open upper half plane, $[(x, y)\colon\ y > 0]$. It is evident that $U \vee \neg U \neq 1$.

EXERCISES

1. Investigate the relations among the sets U, $\neg U$, $\neg\neg U, \ldots,$ for general U.

2. What does the equation $\mathsf{J}UV = 1$, for $\mathsf{J} = \mathsf{DN}$ as before, say about the sets U and V?

3. Show that if we replace E by a topological space in which every set is its own interior: $U = U^*$ for all $U \subseteq E$, then the same definitions as above yield classical sentential logic.

DECIDABILITY AND AXIOMATIZABILITY

We have taken as our central problem that of finding a syntactical definition of the relation of semantic implication. In view of the fact that $p \models q$ iff $\models \mathsf{J}pq$, we may replace this by the problem of characterizing syntactically the set T of valid formulas of a semantically defined theory. There are roughly three things that can happen, which we illustrate with three important examples.

Sentential logic. Here L is a sentential language, and the theory T comprises all valid formulas of L. We have seen that this theory is, in a most reasonable sense, decidable: there is a quite mechanical test which, applied to any formula, tells us whether it is in T. For this reason, a deductive axiomatization of T is something of a luxury, but it is not difficult to give a set of axioms and rules of inference by which all formulas in T and no others are derivable. In fact, such an axiomatization is contained in that for the predicate logic obtained below.

Predicate logic. By *predicate logic* we mean the theory T of all valid formulas in a full language L, as described at the outset. We assume that L has at least one function symbol of rank at least 1, or else one relation symbol of rank at least 2. Then T is not in any reasonable sense decidable; this theorem, of Church, based on Gödel's results, is the last that we shall prove (in outline) in these notes. Nonetheless, we shall see, following Gödel, that there does exist a perfectly satisfactory axiomatization of T by means of axioms and rules of inference, under which exactly the formulas of T are provable.

Arithmetic. We now suppose that our full language L contains particular symbols $=$, 0, 1, $+$, and $\times$, and we consider only interpretations in a single structure N, whose domain is the set of natural numbers $0, 1, 2, \ldots,$ and in which the special symbols receive their usual interpretations. We shall mean by *arithmetic* the theory comprising all formulas of L that are valid under every interpretation in this standard structure. A principal result of Gödel is that arithmetic is not only not decidable, but also not axiomatizable. With arithmetic, then, we have irrevocably failed in our central purpose of providing a syntactical definition of validity, and we can only hope to be the wiser for it.

For the present we shall not give a precise definition of what it means for a set to be *decidable;* it suffices to know that every set that has been claimed to be decidable on intuitive grounds falls within the scope of the definition. Indeed, all proposed definitions of the term have proved equivalent, and we shall give one of these definitions much later, only when it becomes indispensible. But it is easy to give a definition of axiomatizability in terms of decidability; for our purposes the following will do. There is to be given a set of formulas called *axioms* and a relation of finite rank among formulas, whereby a formula is said to follow from others by the *rules of inference.* A finite sequence of formulas is a *proof* iff each formula in it is either an axiom or follows from earlier formulas by the rules of inference; a proof is a *proof of* the last formula in the sequence. A formula that has a proof is a *theorem.* Now it is required that the property of being an axiom, and the relation of following by the rules of inference, be decidable. Then the property of being a proof is also decidable: this is an essential feature of proofs, that any proposed proof can be checked by a decisive test. On the other hand, the axiomatized theory T, comprising all the theorems, need not be decidable: for one may search indefinitely for a proof of a formula without ever coming to know whether or not one exists.

It is a trivial observation that if a theory is decidable then it is axiomatizable: at worst, the criteria for an axiomatization can be met by taking all formulas of the theory as axioms and no rules of inference. On the other hand, we have noted that predicate logic is axiomatizable but not decidable. Moreover, we have noted that arithmetic is not even axiomatizable.

The concept of completeness is related to decidability. A theory T is *complete* if, for each sentence p, either p is in T or $\neg p$ is in T. If an axiomatizable theory T is complete and consistent, then it is decidable. To see this, assume T is axiomatizable, complete, and consistent, and let p be a sentence. It is implicit in the hypothesis of axiomatizability that the formulas of L can be indexed by the natural numbers, and from this it is not difficult to devise an enumeration $s_1, s_2, \ldots$ of all finite sequences of formulas. Since the property of being a proof is decidable, we can sift the list $s_1, s_2, \ldots$, retaining only the proofs, and can write down as long an initial segment as we choose of the resulting list $p_1, p_2, \ldots$ of all proofs. Since T is complete, either p or $\neg p$ is in T. Since T is axiomatizable, whichever is in T has a proof. Thus, for some n, p_n will be, recognizably, a proof for p or for $\neg p$. If p_n is a proof for p, then p is a theorem, that is, p is in T. If p_n is a proof for $\neg p$, then $\neg p$ is in T, and from the consistency of T we conclude that p is not in T. This process clearly lets us decide, in principle, whether arbitrary p is in T.

A theory T defined semantically by reference to a single structure—for example, arithmetic without function or relation symbols other than $0, 1, =, +,$ and $\times$—is automatically complete and consistent. Thus for such theories decidability and axiomatizability coincide.

DECIDABLE THEORIES

It is the exception rather than the rule that a theory of any genuine mathematical complexity is decidable. Nonetheless, there are a few important mathematical theories that have been shown decidable. Most decidability proofs for theories in a language with quantifiers use what has been called the method of *elimination of quantifiers.* We shall illustrate this with two rather simple theories.

Dense linear order. We shall start with a semantic definition of the theory T of dense linear order. Let L be a language with the connectives 0, 1, N, C, D, A, and E, an infinite set V of variables, with no function symbols, and with no relation symbols except $=$, $<$, and $\leq$. We consider only interpretations in the domain R of real numbers under which the relation symbols have their usual meaning. The theory T is the set of all formulas that are valid under every such interpretation. The decision method we shall present was given by Langford; a full discussion is given by Rogers.

We shall show that every formula of the form $p = \mathrm{E}vq$, where q contains no quantifiers, is equivalent to a formula p' without quantifiers, and containing no variables other than those that occur free in p. Since $\mathrm{A}vq \models\!\dashv \neg Ev \neg q$, the same then holds for formulas $p = \mathrm{A}vq$. By repeating this transformation, we can replace any formula p by an equivalent formula p' without quantifiers, and containing no variables other than those that occur free in p. Now if p is a sentence, p' will contain no variables at all, whence it contains no symbols other than 0, 1, N, C, and D. We have seen that it is a trivial matter to reduce such a formula of the sentential logic to an equivalent form 0 or 1. Thus the validity of every sentence can be tested, whereas the validity of a formula p that is not a sentence is equivalent to that of some sentence $\mathrm{A}x_1 \ldots \mathrm{A}x_n p$.

Suppose then that $p = \mathrm{E}vq$ where q contains no quantifiers; clearly we can write q using only the relation symbols $=$ and $<$

and not the symbol $\leq$. We may suppose q in disjunctive form, $q = \bigvee q_i$ where each $q_i = \bigwedge q_{ij}$ and each q_{ij} has one of the forms $x = y$, $x < y$, $\neg(x = y)$, and $\neg(x < y)$. We replace $x \neq y$ by $x < y \vee y < x$, and $x \nless y$ by $x = y \vee y < x$, and multiply out by the law $r \wedge (s \vee t) \models\!\!\!\dashv (r \wedge t) \vee (r \wedge s)$. Then we obtain an equivalent formula q, in disjunctive form, where now each q_{ij} has one of the forms $x = y$ or $x < y$. It is clear that $p = \mathrm{E}v(\bigvee q_i)$ is equivalent to $\bigvee \mathrm{E}vq_i$, whence it will do to consider q_i in place of q, that is, to suppose that $q = \bigwedge q_j$, each q_j some $x = y$ or some $x < y$. Using the fact that, if r does not contain v, $\mathrm{E}v(r \wedge s) \models\!\!\!\dashv r \wedge \mathrm{E}vs$, we can replace p by a formula $p' \wedge \mathrm{E}v \bigwedge q_j$ where now each q_j contains v. Thus we can suppose that $p = \mathrm{E}v \bigwedge q_j$ where each q_j has one of the forms $v = x$, $x < v$, or $v < x$.

Clearly a formula $v = v$ can be deleted without effect, whereas if a formula $v < v$ occurs, p is invalid. If a formula $v = x$ occurs, with x different from v, then p can be given the form $p = \mathrm{E}v[v = x \wedge r(v, x)]$ and is evidently equivalent to $p' = r(x, x)$. Only the case remains that q is a conjunction of formulas $x_1 < v, \ldots, x_m < v$, and $v < y_1, \ldots, v < y_n$ where all the x_i and y_j are different from v. In this case, p is evidently equivalent to p', the conjunction of all the formulas $x_i < y_j$, $1 \leq i \leq m$, $1 \leq j \leq n$. This completes the proof of the decidability of T.

The theory T was defined semantically by reference to the real numbers, but it is clear that exactly the same argument goes through for the rational numbers, or even for the set of those rationals strictly between 0 and 1 that have denominator a power of two. Indeed, in our argument we used of necessity only a finite set of assumptions about the real numbers, which can be expressed by a set A of sentences in L, and the argument therefore holds in any theory that includes A. But now A is a set of axioms for T in the sense that T is precisely the set of all semantic consequences of A. To see this, we note first that since A is included in T, so is the set of all consequences of A; on the other hand, if a formula p is in T, then using only A we can show that p is equivalent to 1, that is, we can establish p as a consequence of A. If we had started with T defined by the set A of axioms, which is perhaps more natural, we should not have known in advance that T is complete, but the proof of decidability shows in fact that every sentence is equivalent, on the assumption of A, to either 0 or 1, hence that either it or its negation belongs to T, and thus shows that T is complete.

If we replace the set of real numbers by the subset of those real x such that $5 \leq x \leq 8$, we obtain a slightly different theory T' which also is decidable. If we adjoin to L two new symbols to denote 5 and 8, the decidability of the resulting theory T'' can be proved by the same method as above, and it follows that the subtheory T' of T'' is also decidable.

EXERCISES.

1. Prove that T' is decidable.

2. Find a set A of axioms for T and an analogous set A' for T'.

Identity theory. Let L have the full set of connectives, an infinite set of variables, no function symbols, and a single relation symbol $=$. We define *identity theory* T to be the set of all formulas that are valid under every interpretation in which the symbol $=$ receives its usual meaning, of identity. It is clear that T cannot be complete since, for each $n > 1$, the sentence C_n: $\mathsf{E}x_i \ldots \mathsf{E}x_n \bigwedge_{1 \leq i < j \leq n} x_i \neq x_j$, asserting of a structure that it contains at least n elements, is valid in some interpretations and not in others. In fact, if we are going to attempt to carry out elimination of quantifiers, we must extend the language L in such a way that the sentences C_n can be written without quantifiers. Let L be extended to a language L' by adjoining an infinite set of relation symbols c_2, $c_3, \ldots$ of rank 0, and extend T to T', the set of formulas valid under all interpretations in which $=$ is interpreted as identity, and each c_n is interpreted in the same way as C_n.

Proceeding as before to eliminate quantifiers, but now using the complete disjunctive form, we are reduced to the case that $p = \mathsf{E}vq$ where, for distinct variables $v, x_1, \ldots, x_n$, q is the conjunction of certain of the equations $v = x_i$ and $x_i = x_j (i < j)$ together with the negations of the rest. The case that q contains any $v = x_i$ can be dealt with as before, and the case that q contains any $x_i = x_j$ similarly. Let $r = \bigwedge_{1 \leq i < j \leq n} x_i \neq x_j$. Then it is evident that $p = \bigwedge$ $\mathsf{E}v(r \wedge v \neq x_1 \wedge \ldots \wedge v \neq x_n$ is equivalent to $p' = r \wedge c_{n+1}$. This completes the elimination of quantifiers, and shows that every sentence of L' is equivalent under T' to a combination of the c_n by means of the connectives. A moment's reflection shows that such a sentence p must express that the cardinal n of the domain lies in a certain set U which is the union of a finite set of disjoint intervals of the form $[n\colon\ a \leq n \leq b]$ or the form $[n\colon\ a \leq n]$. Evidently p is valid iff U consists of the single interval $[n\colon\ 1 \leq n]$. It follows incidentally that no sentence of L' holds for those and only those structures that have a finite domain.

Returning to the theory T, we see that it also is decidable, and indeed we have an algorithm reducing each sentence of L to a sentence, equivalent under the theory, that is a propositional combination of the sentences C_n.

As with the theory of dense linear order, we can obtain from our reasoning a set A of axioms for the theory T. These are simply the sentences asserting that the relation denoted by $=$ is reflexive, symmetric, and transitive:

$$\mathsf{A}x(x = x),\quad \mathsf{A}x\mathsf{A}y(x = y \supset y = x),\ \mathsf{A}x\mathsf{A}y\mathsf{A}z(x = y \wedge y = z \supset x = z).$$

It is worth making the obvious remark that, since any equivalence relation on a set satisfies these axioms, it is impossible within the language L to express conditions that distinguish identity from the other equivalence relations.

EXERCISES

1. Complete the details of the proof that identity theory is decidable.

2. Is there any infinite set P of sentences such that $\phi P = 1$ expresses that the domain of the interpretation ϕ is infinite? Is there any such P expressing that the domain is finite?

Other decidable theories. We mention only two more decidable theories. For each of these the proof of decidability, by elimination of quantifiers, is difficult and depends upon considerable technical knowledge of the theory. The first of these is the theory of Abelian groups, in a language with $=$ and a symbol for the operation of composition in a group. The decision method for this theory, by Szmielew, yields a result analogous to that for identity theory but much more complicated. The other, and perhaps the most important, decision method is that of Tarski for the theory of the real numbers in a language with symbols for equality, addition, and multiplication. This theory is of course complete, and the decision method yields a set of axioms; it has proved useful to know that any property of the reals, expressible in this language, carries over to all other models, the real-closed fields, satisfying these axioms. Tarski's result extends immediately from the real numbers to the complex numbers; by means of analytic geometry it yields also a decision method for a theory of Euclidean geometry.

To see how close real arithmetic is to the edge between decidablity and undecidability, we observe that each natural number n can be characterized within the theory by a formula $p_n(x) = \forall y[xy = y + \dots + y]$ (n terms); on the other hand, if there were a formula $p(x)$ characterizing exactly the set of all natural numbers, it would be possible to translate into the theory every sentence of the arithmetic of the natural numbers, and the undecidability of the theory would follow from that for the natural numbers.

Undecidable theories. There is one set of undecidability results whose proofs are independent of, and perhaps simpler than, Gödel's proof of the undecidability of arithmetic. Results of Post and Turing establish the undecidability of the question of whether an idealized computing machine, given a certain input, will come to the end of its computation; a related result is the unsolvability of the word problem for semigroups: there exist terms $t_1, s_1, \dots, t_n, s_n$ and u in the language of semigroups with $=$ and multiplication, such that the set of those terms w for which the formula $t_1 = s_1 \wedge \dots \wedge t_n = s_n \supset w = u$ is valid, is undecidable. Many other undecidability results are refinements of these, or rather direct applications. One of the most difficult of these results is the proof, by Novikov and Boone, of the unsolvability of the word problem for groups, which settles a well-known and long-unsolved problem.

AXIOMATIZATION OF PREDICATE LOGIC

The remainder of these notes will be devoted first to proving that predicate logic is axiomatizable and second to outlining a proof that arithmetic is not axiomatizable, with the consequence that neither it nor predicate logic is decidable. We shall of course mention related results as we go.

By *predicate logic* we mean the theory T of all formulas of some language L, as described at the outset, that hold under every interpretation. We shall give two rather different axiomatizations for this theory. The first is a traditional axiomatization, not differing essentially from that used by Russell and Whitehead. The fact that the axioms and rules of this axiomatization do in fact give a syntactical characterization of the semantically defined theory T is commonly called Gödel's Completeness Theorem; since we have used the word completeness in a different sense, we shall call this the Adequacy Theorem. The argument used here is a refinement by Henkin of Gödel's proof. The second axiomatization, by Gentzen, is less familiar, but possesses a certain naturalness, as well as various technical advantages. We shall give a proof of the adequacy of Gentzen's system that is due to Rasiowa and Sikorski.

It will be convenient to take as the connectives of L only 0, J, and A, and to view the others as abbreviations, in particular, $\neg p$ for $p \supset 0$ and Ex for $\neg$ Ax $\neg$. We assume then that L has the connectives 0, J, A, an infinite set V of variables, and an entirely arbitrary collection of function and relation symbols of various ranks.

We now describe the first axiomatization. The *axioms* are given by five schemes, each comprising all formulas of the prescribed form. The *axiom schemes* are as follows:

*A*1. $p \supset (q \supset p)$;

*A*2. $[p \supset (q \supset r)] \supset [(p \supset q) \supset (p \supset r)]$;

*A*3. $[(p \supset 0) \supset 0] \supset p;$

*A*4. $\mathsf{A}x(p \supset q) \supset (p \supset \mathsf{A}xq)$ where x does not occur free in p;

*A*5. $\mathsf{A}xp(x) \supset p(t)$.

We recall that the notation used in *A*5 implies that $p(x)$ is a formula and $p(t)$ the formula obtained from $p(x)$ by replacing the variable x by the term t at every free occurrence, and that no occurrence of t introduced thus in $p(t)$ contains a bound occurrence of a variable.

There are two *rules of inference.* The first, *Modus ponens,* is a ternary relation which holds between two formulas as *premises* and a third as *conclusion* iff the premises are of the form p and $p \supset q$, and the conclusion is q. The second, *Generalization,* relates a single premise to a conclusion, and holds iff the premise has the form $p(x)$ and the conclusion the form $\mathsf{A}yp(y)$. We indicate these rules schematically as follows:

$$\frac{p \mid p \supset q}{q} \quad \text{(MP)}; \qquad \frac{p(x)}{\mathsf{A}yp(y)} \quad \text{(GN)}.$$

A *derivation* from a set P of formulas as premises to a formula q as conclusion is a finite sequence $D = (d_1, \ldots, d_n)$ of formulas such that each d_i either is an axiom or a member of P or is the conclusion by a rule of inference from earlier d_j, d_k as premises, and such that d_n is q, *provided* that, in an application of GN, the variable x does not occur free in P. We write $P \vdash q$ iff there exists a derivation of q from P or any subset of P. [The last phrase is a technicality to avoid an artificial restriction on the use of GN in the case that all but a finite number of the variables occur free in P.]

A *proof* of q is a derivation of q from the empty set of formulas; note that here the restriction on GN disappears. We write $\vdash q$, and call q a *theorem,* iff there exists a proof of q.

If $P \vdash 0$ we call P *deductively inconsistent,* or contradictory; otherwise P is *deductively consistent.*

There are three easy consequences of the axioms and rules that we shall need later. Little would be lost by simply adding them to the list of axioma and rules, but we shall give proofs of them, as illustrations of the concepts of derivation and proof.

PROPOSITION. For all formulas p, $\vdash p \supset p$.

A scheme for a proof $D = (d_1, \ldots, d_5)$ of all such formulas $p \supset p$ is exhibited, with notations in the right margin to indicate how each line conforms to the conditions on a proof. The scheme follows:

d_1	$p \supset (p \supset p)$	$A1$
d_2	$p \supset ((p \supset p) \supset p)$	$A1$
d_3	$[p \supset ((p \supset p) \supset p)] \supset [(p \supset (p \supset p)) \supset (p \supset p)]$	$A2$
d_4	$(p \supset (p \supset p)) \supset (p \supset p)$	d_2, d_3, MP
d_5	$p \supset p$	d_1, d_4, MP

PROPOSITION. For all formulas p and q, $\vdash (q \supset 0) \supset (q \supset p)$.

A proof follows:

d_1	$((p \supset 0) \supset 0) \supset p$	$A3$
d_2	$[((p \supset 0) \supset 0) \supset p] \supset [0 \supset [((p \supset 0) \supset 0) \supset p]]$	$A1$
d_3	$0 \supset [((p \supset 0) \supset 0) \supset p]$	d_1, d_2, MP
d_4	$[0 \supset [((p \supset 0) \supset 0) \supset pp]] \supset [[0 \supset ((p \supset 0) \supset 0)] \supset (0 \supset p)]$	$A2$
d_5	$[0 \supset ((p \supset 0) \supset 0)] \supset (0 \supset p)$	d_3, d_4, MP
d_6	$0 \supset ((p \supset 0) \supset 0)$	$A1$
d_7	$0 \supset p$	d_5, d_6, MP
d_8	$(0 \supset p) \supset (q \supset (0 \supset p))$	$A1$
d_9	$q \supset (0 \supset p)$	d_7, d_8, MP
d_{10}	$(q \supset (0 \supset p)) \supset ((q \supset 0) \supset (q \supset p))$	$A2$
d_{11}	$(q \supset 0) \supset (q \supset p)$	d_9, d_{10}, MP

PROPOSITION. For all formulas p, $\neg\neg \mathsf{A}x \neg\neg p \vdash \mathsf{A}xp$.

We are supposing the other connectives defined in terms of 0, J, and A; in particular we have taken $\neg p$ as an abbreviation for $p \supset 0$, and $\mathsf{E}xp$ as an abbreviation for $\neg \mathsf{A}x \neg p$. The proposition asserts then that $\neg \mathsf{E}x \neg p \vdash \mathsf{A}xp$. This is shown by the following derivation scheme.

d_1	$\neg\neg \mathsf{A}x \neg\neg p$	Premise
d_2	$(\neg\neg \mathsf{A}x \neg\neg p) \supset (\mathsf{A}x \neg\neg p)$	A3
d_3	$\mathsf{A}x \neg\neg p$	d_1, d_2, MP
d_4	$\mathsf{A}x \neg\neg p \supset \neg\neg p$	A5
d_5	$\neg\neg p$	d_3, d_4, MP
d_6	$\neg\neg p \supset p$	A3
d_7	p	d_5, d_6, MP
d_8	$\mathsf{A}xp$	d_7, GN.

For the justification of the last line, under GN, it is essential that the variable x does not in fact occur free in the single premise for the derivation, $\neg\neg \mathsf{A}x \neg\neg p$.

It is a somewhat awkward fact that if D_1 is a derivation from P to q, and D_2 a derivation from $\{q\} \cup R$ to s, then the sequence D of formulas obtained by following D_1 by D_2 need not be a derivation from $P \cup R$ to s. For the rule GN may be applied in D_1 to a variable that occurs free in $\{q\} \cup R$, although not in P, or in D_2 to a variable that occurs free in P although not in $q \cup R$. Nonetheless, the relation $\vdash$ is transitive in the sense of the following propositions.

PROPOSITION. If $P \vdash Q$ and $Q \cup R \vdash S$, then $P \cup R \vdash S$.

This follows readily from the case that P and R are finite, that Q consists of a single formula q, and S of a single formula s. We suppose then that D_1 is a derivation from P to q and that D_2 is a derivation from $\{q\} \cup R$ to s. Only a finite number of variables can occur free in the finite set $P \cup \{q\} \cup R$ of formulas, whence the set V' of the remaining variables is infinite. Suppose now D_1 contains an inference by GN from some $p(x)$ to $\mathsf{A}yp(y)$, and hence that x does not occur free in P. Then some subsequence E of D_1, ending with this inference, constitutes a derivation from P to $\mathsf{A}yp(y)$. If we form E' from E by replacing every free occurrence of x by an occurrence of a new variable x' from V', and adjoin E' to D_1, we have now a derivation D_1' from P to q in which $\mathsf{A}yp(y)$ is justified by application of GN to $p(x')$ where x' is in V'. Repeating this construction, we obtain a derivation D_1'' from P to q in which GN is applied to a formula $\mathsf{A}yp(y)$ only for variables x from V'. We may modify D_2 similarly to obtain D_2'' with the property that GN is applied to formulas $p(x)$ only for variables x that do not occur in $P \cup \{q\} \cup R$. If we now form D'' by following D_1'' by D_2'', all applications of GN in D'' will be justified, giving a derivation from P to s, as required.

EXERCISES

1. Show by example that the product D of two derivations D_1 and D_2, as above, need not be a derivation.

2. Complete the proof of the proposition by showing that the general case in the statement of the proposition follows from the special case treated in the proof.

Another remark in the same vein, which we shall use later, is that if P is a set of formulas in L and q a formula in L, and if L' is a language obtained by adding further symbols to L, then the relation $P \vdash q$ holds with respect to L iff it holds with respect to L'. This remark is an easy step in the direction of a deeper theorem of Craig, discussed later.

We remark also that it is obviously decidable whether a given formula is an axiom, whether a given formula follows from other given formulas by a rule of inference, and hence whether a given sequence of formulas is a derivation from a given set P of formulas to a given formula q.

EXERCISES

1. Prove the first of the preceding remarks.

2. Describe explicitly a method of deciding, given a set P of formulas, a formula q, and a sequence $p_1, \ldots, p_n$ of formulas, whether this sequence is a derivation from P to q.

VALIDITY OF THE AXIOMATIZATION

PROPOSITION. If $P \vdash q$, then $P \models q$.

This proposition merely asserts that we have not overreached ourselves in choosing axioms and rules of inference; its proof, to which we turn in a moment, is not difficult. The converse proposition, that we have not been too modest in our choice of axioms and rules, is not obvious, and the proof that we shall give for it below is far more difficult.

Arguing by induction on the length of a derivation, we are left with two things to prove. First, we must show that every axiom is valid. Second, we must show that if the premises to an inference by one of the rules, in a derivation from P, are semantic consequences of P, then the conclusion also is a semantic consequence of P.

It is immediately evident that every axiom falling under one of the schemes $A1$, $A2$, $A3$ is valid.

For the scheme $A4$ we must show that if ϕ is any interpretation, and if x is not free in p, then $\phi[\mathsf{A}x(p \supset q)] = 1$ implies that $\phi[p \supset \mathsf{A}xq] = 1$. In other words, assuming $\phi[\mathsf{A}x(p \supset q)] = 1$ and $\phi p = 1$, we must show that $\phi \mathsf{A}xq = 1$. Let ϕ' be any interpretation that agrees with ϕ on $\mathsf{V} \cup \mathsf{R} \cup \mathsf{F}$ except possibly on x; then we must show that $\phi' q = 1$. From $\phi[\mathsf{A}x(p \supset q)] = 1$ we have $\phi'(p \supset q) = 1$. Since x is not free in p, we have $\phi' p = \phi p$, whence from $\phi p = 1$ we have $\phi' p = 1$. But now $\phi'(p \supset q) = 1$ and $\phi' p = 1$ give $\phi' q = 1$.

For $A5$, from $\phi[\mathsf{A}xp(x)] = 1$ we must conclude that $\phi p(t) = 1$. There exists an interpretation ϕ' that agrees with ϕ on $\mathsf{V} \cup \mathsf{F} \cup \mathsf{R}$ except possibly on x, where $\phi' x = \phi t$. By an earlier proposition about substitution, $\phi' p(x) = \phi p(t)$. But $\phi \mathsf{A}xp(x) = 1$ implies that $\phi' p(x) = 1$, whence $\phi p(t) = 1$.

Modus ponens presents no difficulty. If $\phi p = 1$ and $\phi(p \supset q) = 1$ for every ϕ such that $\phi P = 1$, then $\phi q = 1$ for every such ϕ.

For Generalization, suppose that $P \vdash p(x)$, where x does not occur free in P. We must show that $\phi P = 1$ implies $\phi Ayp(y) = 1$. Let ϕ' agree with ϕ on $\mathsf{V} \cup \mathsf{F} \cup \mathsf{R}$ except possibly on x. Since x is not free in P, $\phi' P = \phi P = 1$ and $\phi' p(x) = 1$. This shows that $\phi Axp(x) = 1$, and, by a proposition on substitution, $\phi Ayp(y) = \phi Axp(x) = 1$.

COROLLARY. Every theorem is valid: if $\vdash p$, then $\models p$.

COROLLARY. If a set of formulas has a model, then it is deductively consistent.

EXERCISE. Construct examples to show the condition on the variable x in A4 and also that in the use of GN in a derivation cannot be dropped.

THE DEDUCTION THEOREM

The Deduction Theorem is the first major step toward the proof of the adequacy of the axiomatization. The connective $\supset$ was defined in such a way that $\models p \supset q$ iff $p \models q$. We want the deductive counterpart, that $\vdash p \supset q$ iff $p \vdash q$. One half of this is essentially the content of the rule Modus ponens: if $\vdash p \supset q$, then $p \vdash q$. The other half, that $p \vdash q$ implies $\vdash p \supset q$, is the main content of the Deduction Theorem.

DEDUCTION THEOREM. Let P be a set of formulas, and let q and r be formulas. Then $P \vdash q \supset r$ iff $P, q \vdash r$.

That $P \vdash q \supset r$ implies $P, q \vdash r$ follows directly by MP and the transitivity of implication. Given a derivation from P to $q \supset r$, we obtain from it a derivation from $P \cup \{q\}$ to r by adding final lines q and r, and justifying the first as a premise and the second as the conclusion from the two preceding lines $q \supset r$ and q by MP.

For the converse, suppose given a derivation $D = (d_1, \ldots, d_n)$ from $P \cup \{q\}$ to $d_n = r$. Let D' be the sequence $D = (d'_1, \ldots, d'_n)$ where each $d'_i = q \supset d_i$ and, in particular, $d'_n = q \supset r$. Now D' as it stands is not quite a derivation from premises P to $q \supset r$, but we shall show how to convert it into such a derivation by the insertion of additional lines before each d'_i. For the inductive argument, we can suppose this already done for $d'_1, \ldots, d'_{i-1}$. We proceed by cases.

Case 1. If $d_i = q$, then $d'_i = q \supset q$ has been shown to be a theorem, and a proof of it may be inserted.

Case 2. If d_i is an axiom or a member of P, we insert two lines: $e = d_i$ and $f = d_i \supset (q \supset d_i)$. Here e is justified as an axiom or member of P, f is an axiom under $A2$, and $d'_i = q \supset d_i$ follows from e and f by MP.

Case 3. Suppose that d_i follows from two earlier lines d_j and $d_k = d_j \supset d_i$ by MP. We insert two lines, $e = d'_k \supset (d'_j \supset d'_i)$ and $f = d'_j \supset d'_i$. Now $e = [q \supset (d_j \supset d_i)] \supset [(q \supset d_j) \supset (q \supset d_i)]$ falls under $A2$, and f follows from d'_k and e by MP. Finally, d'_i follows from d'_j and f by MP.

Case 4. Suppose d_i follows from an earlier line d_j by GN, hence $d_j = p(x)$ and $d_i = \mathsf{A}yp(y)$ where x is not free in $P \cup \{q\}$. We insert two lines: $e = \mathsf{A}y(q \supset p(y))$ and $f = \mathsf{A}y(q \supset p(y)) \supset (q \supset \mathsf{A}yp(y))$. Now e follows from $d'_j = q \supset p(x)$ by GN, since x is not free in $P \cup \{q\}$, and f falls under $A5$ *provided* y *is not free in* q, so that $d'_i = q \supset \mathsf{A}xp(y)$ follows by MP. [If y is free in q, we can establish $q \supset \mathsf{A}zp(z)$ for some new variable z; then, first establishing $\mathsf{A}zp(z) \supset \mathsf{A}yp(y)$, we can easily obtain d'_i.]

EXERCISE

1. Supply the missing details at the end of Case 4.

2. There is some advantage for the axiomatization, at the cost of some complication in the definition of formula and interpretation, to use two different sets of symbols for bound and free variables; if this is done, the accidental complication in Case 4 does not arise. Indicate how the development so far could be revised in accordance with this suggestion.

THE CONSISTENCY THEOREM

We shall see later that the next theorem, which we shall call the Consistency Theorem, is hardly more than a restatement of the Adequacy Theorem.

CONSISTENCY THEOREM. A set of formulas is deductively consistent iff it has a model.

Half of this was established as a corollary to the validity of the axiomatization. It remains, given a (deductively) consistent set P of formulas in a language L, to find an interpretation ϕ such that $\phi P = 1$. We must construct the interpretation out of the only material that is given us, the language L and the set P of formulas. Roughly, the elements of the structure will be the terms of L, the functions will be the operations of the algebra of terms, and the relations of the structure will be determined in accordance with the set P of formulas. This construction of an interpretation for L out of materials found in L itself is somewhat similar to the representation of an abstract group by permutations on a domain whose elements are exactly those of the given group.

There are two difficulties that must be overcome. First, L may not have enough terms for the set of all terms to provide a domain for an interpretation ϕ such that $\phi P = 1$. It may be that $\exists x p(x)$ is in P and yet $\neg p(t)$ is in P for every term t of L. To remedy this, we extend L by adding new terms. Second, P may not be large enough to determine fully the structure we want to impose on the set of terms. There may well be an atomic formula p such that neither p nor $\neg p$ is in P. To remedy this, we extend P to a larger consistent set. We shall show below how to overcome each of these difficulties separately, and then both at once. After this we have no trouble in constructing the interpretation ϕ.

We begin the proof. We shall consider two conditions on a set P of formulas in a language L:

(1) for every formula p in L, either p or $\neg p$ is in P, but not both;

(2) if a formula $\exists x p(x)$ is in P, then there is some term t in L such that $p(t)$ is in P.

LEMMA. Every consistent set P of formulas in L is contained in a consistent set P' of formulas in L that satisfies (1).

We suppose the formulas of L well ordered, using, if necessary, the Axiom of Choice, or else we invoke directly Zorn's Lemma, which is equivalent to the Axiom of Choice. Zorn's Lemma asserts the following.

Let F be a family of subsets Q of some set S with the property that if $G \subseteq F$ is a chain, that is, Q_1 and Q_2 in G implies $Q_1 \subseteq Q_2$ or $Q_2 \subseteq Q_1$, then the union of all the Q in G belongs to F. Then F contains a maximal element M, that is, such that Q in F and $M \subseteq Q$ implies $M = Q$.

To apply this, we take F to be the family of all consistent sets Q of formulas of L such that $P \subseteq Q$. Evidently the union U of a chain $G \subseteq F$ contains P. We show that U is consistent. If U were not consistent, that is, if $U \vdash 0$, then $p_1, \ldots, p_n \vdash 0$ for some finite set of formulas $p_1, \ldots, p_n$ in U. Since U is the union of the Q in G, each p_i is in some Q_i in G; since G is a chain, some Q_i, $1 \leq i \leq n$, contains the rest, and hence $p_1, \ldots, p_n$ are in this Q_i. But then $Q_i \vdash 0$, contrary to the assumption that all Q in F are consistent. We have shown that U is in G, and the hypothesis of Zorn's Lemma is satisfied. It follows that F contains a maximal set P'.

To prove (1), suppose there is some formula p such that neither p nor $\neg p$ is in P'. Since P' is maximal among consistent sets containing P, we conclude that $P' \cup \{p\} \vdash 0$ and $P' \cup \{\neg p\} \vdash 0$. By the Deduction Theorem, $P' \vdash \neg p$ and $P' \vdash \neg\neg p$. But from $\neg p = p \supset 0$ and $\neg\neg p = (p \supset 0) \supset 0$, by MP we have 0, whence $P' \vdash 0$, contrary to hypothesis.

An extension L' of a language L shall mean here a language that differs from L only in possessing a possibly larger set of variables.

> LEMMA. If P is a consistent set of formulas in a language L, then there exists a consistent set P' of formulas containing P in an extension L' of L, such that $\mathrm{E}xq(x)$ in P implies some $q(t)$ is in P'.

For each formula $p = \mathrm{E}xq(x)$ in P we adjoin a new variable v_p to L and a new formula $q(v_p)$ to P. This process clearly yields a set P' in a language L' such that $P \subseteq P'$ and that, for every $\mathrm{E}xq(x)$ in P, some $q(v)$ is in P'. To show that P' is consistent it suffices to consider, first, the case of a finite number of adjunctions, and, therefore, that of a single adjunction. We must show that if P is consistent, if $\mathrm{E}xq(x)$ is in P, and if v does not occur in P, then $P \cup \{q(v)\}$ is consistent.

Suppose $P, q(v) \vdash 0$. By the Deduction Theorem, $P \vdash \neg q(v)$. Since v does not occur in P, by GN we have $P \vdash \mathrm{A}x \neg q(x)$. But P contains $\mathrm{E}xq(x)$, that is, $\neg \mathrm{A}x \neg q(x) = (\mathrm{A}x \neg q(x)) \supset 0$. By MP we conclude that $P \vdash 0$, contrary to hypothesis.

> LEMMA. If P is a consistent set of formulas in a language L, then there exists a consistent set P' of formulas containing P in an extension L' of L, such that P' and L' satisfy (1) and (2).

We construct a sequence of languages $L_1, L_2, \ldots$ and a sequence of sets of formulas $P_1, Q_1, P_2, Q_2, \ldots$ as follows. We begin with $L_1 = L$ and $P_1 = P$. Suppose now a consistent set P_n of formulas in L_n is given. By the first lemma we can take Q_n in L_n, consistent, containing P_n, and satisfying (1). By the second lemma we can find an extension L_{n+1} of L_n, and a consistent set P_{n+1} in L_{n+1} containing Q_n and such that $\exists xq(x)$ in P_n implies some $q(t)$ is in P_{n+1}. We now take L' to be the language whose symbols are all those in the L_n, and we define P' in L' to be the union of the sets P_n.

Clearly P' contains P and, as the union of a chain of consistent sets, is consistent. If p is any formula of L', then p is a formula of some L_n, and, since P_n satisfies (1), either p or $\neg p$ is in P_n. But then p or $\neg p$ is in P'. Thus P' and L' satisfy (1). If $p = \exists xq(x)$ is in P, it is in some P_n. It follows that $q(v)$ is in Q_{n+1} for some v in L_{n+1}. But then $q(v)$ is in P_{n+1} and so in P' for some v in L', and (2) is satisfied.

To complete the proof of the Consistency Theorem, we need an interpretation ϕ of L such that $\phi P = 1$. It is clear that we may replace P and L by P' and L' as in the preceding lemma, and thus we may assume (1) and (2).

For the domain of ϕ we take the set T of all terms of L. If f is a function symbol of rank n, we define the function ϕf by setting $(\phi f)(t_1, \ldots, t_n) = f t_1 \ldots t_n$, for all $t_1, \ldots, t_n$ in T. If x is in V, we define $\phi x = x$. It now follows by induction that $\phi t = t$ for all t in T. If r is a relation symbol of rank n, we define ϕr by setting $(\phi r)(t_1, \ldots, t_n) = 1$ iff $r t_1 \ldots t_n$ is in P. This completes the definition of ϕ, and it remains to show that $\phi P = 1$.

We show, by induction on the number of connectives in p, that $\phi p = 1$ iff p is in P. This follows immediately from the definition if p is an atomic formula, and is trivial if p is 0. Let $p = q \supset r$. Assume first that $\phi p = 1$, hence either $\phi q = 0$ or $\phi r = 1$. By the induction hypothesis, $\phi q = 0$ implies that q is not in P, whence, by (1), $\neg q$ is in P. We saw earlier that $(q \supset 0) \vdash (q \supset r)$, that is, $\neg q \vdash (q \supset r)$, whence from $\neg q$ in P we have $P \vdash q \supset r$. As before, it follows that $\neg(q \supset r)$ is not in P, hence $q \supset r$ is in P. If $\phi r = 1$, we reason similarly that r is in P, and, from $r \vdash (q \supset r)$, that $P \vdash q \supset r$ and $q \supset r$ is in P. In either case, we have p in P. Assume for the converse that p is in P. From $\phi q = 1$ we must infer that $\phi r = 1$, that is, from q in P we must infer that r is in P. By MP, $q \supset r$ in P and q in P yield $P \vdash r$, whence r is in P.

The case remains that $p = \mathsf{A}xq(x)$. Assume first that p is not in P. We saw that $\neg \mathsf{E}x \neg q(x) \vdash \mathsf{A}xq(x)$, whence it follows that $\neg \mathsf{E}x \neg q(x)$ is not in P and hence, by (1), that $\mathsf{E}x \neg q(x)$ is in P. By (2) it follows that $\neg q(t)$ is in P for some t, and hence, by (1), that $q(t)$ is not in P. By the induction hypothesis it follows that $\phi q(t) = 0$, and from this that $\phi p = \phi \mathsf{A}xq(x) = 0$, as required.

Assume now that $p = \mathsf{A}xq(x)$ and $\phi p = 0$. Then $\phi' q(x) = 0$ for some interpretation ϕ' that agrees with ϕ on $\mathsf{V} \cup \mathsf{F} \cup \mathsf{R}$ except possibly on x. Then $\phi' x = t$, an element of T. Let $q'(x)$ be obtained from $q(x)$ by relettering the bound variables so that no variable in t occurs bound in $q'(x)$; then we may substitute t for x to obtain $q'(t)$. Since ϕ' agrees with ϕ except possibly on x, and $\phi' x = t = \phi t$, it follows by a proposition on substitution that $\phi' q'(x) = \phi q'(t)$. Now it is routine to show that $\phi' q'(x) = \phi' q(x)$, and also that $\mathsf{A}xq(x) \vdash \mathsf{A}xq'(x)$. From the first we have that $\phi' q'(x) = \phi' q(x) = 0$, whence $\phi q'(t) = 0$, and, by the induction hypothesis, $q'(t)$ is not in P. From the second, using $A5$ and MP, we conclude that $\mathsf{A}xp(x) \vdash q'(t)$. By (1), since $q'(t)$ is not in P, it follows that $\mathsf{A}xq(x)$ is not in P, as required.

It is a commonplace in abstract mathematics to prove the (deductive) consistency of a theory by exhibiting a model. The less obvious half of the Consistency Theorem, that every deductively consistent theory has a model, is less commonly used, perhaps because mathematicians are less concerned about existence: indeed, the Consistency Theorem might be viewed as a modest but precise expression of the rather sweeping claim that mathematical existence is nothing more than consistency.

The usefulness of the Consistency Theorem in establishing the consistency of a theory is rather limited, since the construction of a model ordinarily requires assumptions in the metalanguage far stronger than those expressed by the object theory. An alternative way of establishing consistency of an axiomatic theory is to show by purely syntactical considerations that, say, the formula $\mathsf{0}$ cannot be proved in the theory. But this also has proved of only limited usefulness. We shall see later that a theorem of Gödel leaves little hope of proving the consistency of a theory except by assuming in the metalanguage a theory that is at least as strong. Any assurance of the consistency of reasonably complex mathematical theories would seem in the end to reduce to some combination of basic intuition with experimental evidence.

THE ADEQUACY THEOREM AND COMPACTNESS THEOREM

ADEQUACY THEOREM. If P is any set of formulas and q is any formula, then $P \vdash q$ iff $P \models q$.

Taking q to be 0 gives the Consistency Theorem. To prove the Adequacy Theorem, in view of the Validity Theorem, we need only show that $P \models q$ implies $P \vdash q$. Assuming $P \models q$, it is immediate that $P, \neg q \models 0$. By the Consistency Theorem, this gives $P, \neg q \vdash 0$. By the Deduction Theorem, this gives $P \vdash \neg\neg q$. Using the axiom $((q \supset 0) \supset 0) \supset q$, that is, $\neg\neg q \supset q$, and MP, we conclude that $P \vdash q$.

We have already used the trivial observation, which follows immediately from the definition of a derivation, that $P \vdash q$ iff $P_0 \vdash q$ for some finite subset P_0 of P. By the Adequacy Theorem we may translate this trivial observation into a semantic theorem that is by no means obvious.

COMPACTNESS THEOREM. If $P \models q$, then $P_0 \models q$ for some finite subset P_0 of P.

COROLLARY. A set P has a model iff every finite subset has a model.

The word compactness is borrowed from topology, for the reasons that follow. Let E be the set of all interpretations of a language L. [All interpretations with domain included in some fixed, sufficiently large set will do.] A subset U of E is called *closed* iff, for some set P of formulas, ϕ is in U iff $\phi P = 1$. The set E, together with the family F of all its closed subsets, constitutes a *topological space*. A space E is called *compact* if it has the finite intersection porperty for closed sets: if F is any collection of closed sets such that no finite number of members of F has empty intersection, then the intersection of all the sets in F is not empty. Now the Compactness Theorem, or rather the corollary, which is easily seen equivalent to it, asserts that the space E of interpretations is compact.

We have seen directly earlier that no sentence of identity theory is satisfied exactly by all finite structures. A rather simple application of the Compactness Theorem permits us to draw the same conclusion for other theories. For example, let T be the theory of groups, with symbols for equality and group composition, and suppose a sentence q holds in all infinite groups. Then $P \models q$ where P consists of sentences $p_2, p_3, \ldots$ and each p_n asserts the existence of at least n elements. By the Compactness Theorem we conclude that some finite subset P_0 of P implies q, whence some $p_n \models q$. Thus a sentence true for all infinite groups is true for all groups of sufficiently large finite order.

EXERCISES

1. Examine E more closely as a topological space.

2. If E is the space of interpretations and F the set of formulas of L, we have two maps between the set $S(E)$ of all subsets of E and the set $S(F)$ of all subsets of F: for $U \subseteq E$ define αU to be the set of all p in F such that $\phi p = 1$ for all ϕ in U; for $V \subseteq F$, define βV to be the set of all ϕ in E such that $\phi p = 1$ for all p in V. How are these two maps related? In particular, how is $\beta\alpha U$ related to U, and $\alpha\beta V$ to V? What does it mean if $\beta\alpha U = U$, if $\alpha\beta V = V$? What can be said of $\alpha\beta\alpha U$, of $\beta\alpha\beta V$?

3. Assume that every non constant polynomial with coefficients in a given field has a root in some larger field. Use the Compactness Theorem to conclude that there is some field containing the rationals in which every non constant polynomial with rational coefficients has a root.

4. Find other applications of the Compactness Theorem to familiar mathematical questions. [For this and related ideas, see the book of Robinson.]

PREDICATE LOGIC WITH IDENTITY

We denote by $=$ one of the binary relation symbols of L, and use the customary notation $t = s$ instead of $=ts$. Let I_0 be the set of *proper interpretations* ϕ under which $=$ is interpreted by identity on the domain of ϕ, that is, such that $\phi(t = s) = 1$ iff $\phi t = \phi s$. We say that P *properly implies* q, $P \models_{I_0} q$, if $\phi P = 1$ implies $\phi q = 1$ for all ϕ in I_0. If $\models_{I_0} q$ we call q *properly valid*, and if $P \models_{I_0} 0$ we call P *properly consistent*. We shall axiomatize the theory T_{I_0} of all properly valid formulas.

We add to the set A of axioms all those in the set I given by the following schemes:

$I1.$ $t = t;$

$I2.$ $t = s \supset s = t;$

$I3.$ $t = s \wedge s = u \supset t = u;$

$I4.$ $t_i = t_i' \supset ft_1 \ldots t_n = ft_1 \ldots t_{i-1}t_i't_{i+1} \ldots t_n$, for each f in F_n and each i, $1 \leq i \leq n;$

$I5.$ $t_i = t_i' \supset (rt_1 \ldots t_n \supset rt_1 \ldots t_{i-1}t_i't_{i+1} \ldots t_r)$ for each r in R_n and each i, $1 \leq i \leq n.$

EXERCISE. Show that $I2$ and $I3$ are redundant.

The rules of inference are unchanged, and the relation $P \vdash_{I_0} q$ is defined exactly as $P \vdash q$, but with the set $A \cup I$ of axioms in place of the set A. Evidently $P \vdash_{I_0} q$ iff $P \cup I \vdash q$.

ADEQUACY THEOREM FOR PREDICATE LOGIC WITH IDENTITY. If P is a set of formulas and q a formula, then $P \vdash_{I_0} q$ iff $P \models_{I_0} q$.

It is clear that the axioms of the set I are properly valid, whence $P \vdash_{I_0} q$ implies $P \models_{I_0} q$. For the converse, it will do to show that if P is properly consistent it has a proper model. Suppose P is properly consistent. Then $P \cup I$ is consistent and, by the Consistency Theorem, has an ordinary model ϕ, with some domain A. From $\phi I = 1$ we know that $\phi(=)$ is an equivalence relation $\equiv$ on A, and that this relation is substitutive with respect to all the functions ϕf and relations ϕr on A. It follows that on the set $[A]$ of cosets of A under $\equiv$ there exist uniquely determined functions ψf and relations ψr such that, if f is in F_n,

$$(\psi f)([a_1], \ldots, [a_n]) = [(\phi f)(a_1, \ldots, a_n)] \text{ for all } a_1, \ldots, a_n \text{ in } A,$$

and, if r is in R_n,

$$(\psi r)([a_1], \ldots, [a_n]) = (\phi f)(a_1, \ldots, a_n) \text{ for all } a_1, \ldots, a_n \text{ in } A.$$

We define a new interpretation ψ with domain $[A]$ by taking $\psi x = [\phi x]$ for x in V, and the ψf, f in F, and ψr, r in R, as above. From the definition of the ψf it follows by induction that $\psi t = [\phi t]$ for all terms t. From the definition of the ψr it follows directly that $\psi p = \phi p$ for p an atomic formula, and it now follows by induction that $\psi p = \phi p$ for all formulas p. In particular, we conclude that $\psi P = \phi P = 1$, whence ψ is a model for P.

It remains to show that ψ is a proper interpretation. Suppose $\psi(t = s) = 1$. Then $\phi(t = s) = 1$, whence ϕt and ϕs stand in the relation $\phi(=)$, that is, $\phi t \equiv \phi s$. But then ϕt and ϕs belong to the same coset: $[\phi t] = [\phi s]$. Since $\psi t = [\phi t]$ and $\psi s = [\phi s]$, we have $\psi t = \psi s$. In all, this shows that the interpretation $\psi(=)$ of $=$

under ψ is the identity on $[A]$, hence that ψ is proper.

THE LÖWENHEIM SKOLEM THEOREM

THEOREM. Let P be a set of formulas in a language L with identity symbol, and let n be the cardinal of the set of those symbols that occur in P. If P has an infinite proper model, and m is any infinite cardinal, $m \geq n$, then P has a proper model of cardinal m.

This theorem will be obtained by a closer examination of the proof of the Consistency Theorem. To begin, we discard from L all symbols except the connectives and the symbol $=$ that do not occur in P, and then adjoin an infinite set M of variables, of cardinal m. Then, since $n \leq m$, L has in all m symbols and the same number of formulas. We now form a set P' by adjoining to P the set I of axioms for identity, and also all the formulas $x \neq y$ for pairs of distinct variables x and y from M. If P' were inconsistent, then $P \cup I$ together with some finite set of the formulas $x \neq y$ would be inconsistent. But it is clear that such a set can be realized in any infinite proper model for P by distinct choice of the finite number of ϕx and ϕy involved. Thus P' is consistent, and we replace P by P'; that is, we assume that P contains I and all the $x \neq y$ for distinct x and y from M.

We now construct the L_n, P_n, and Q_n as in the proof of the Consistency Theorem. First, L_1 has m symbols and m formulas. Suppose L_n has cardinal m. Then L_n has at most m formulas $p = \mathsf{E}xq(x)$, whence L_{n+1} is obtained from L_n by adding at most m new variables. It follows that L_{n+1} also has cardinal m. Since the union of a countable number of sets of cardinal m again has cardinal m, it follows that L', as the union of the L_n, has cardinal m, and, since it contains the set M, has exactly m terms.

The interpretation ϕ, obtained from P' and L', then has domain of cardinal m. Since $\phi I = 1$, ϕ determines a proper interpretation, $[\phi]$, whose domain then has cardinal at most m. If x and y are distinct elements of M, then the formula $x \neq y$ is in P, and, since $[\phi]P = 1$, $[\phi]x \neq [\phi]y$. Thus $[\phi]$ maps the set M one to one into the domain of $[\phi]$, which therefore has cardinal exactly m.

COROLLARY. If P is any countable or finite set of formulas in a language L with identity symbol, and P has an infinite proper model, then P has proper models of every infinite cardinality.

The Löwenheim Skolem has startling consequences of two kinds, one showing that a theory has unexpectedly large models, and the other that it has unexpectedly small models.

As an example of the first kind, consider any set A of axioms for the natural numbers that can be formulated in a language L with the symbol $=$, symbols $+$ and $\times$, and possibly other arithmetical symbols. We assume that the axioms are valid under the standard interpretation, in the domain N of the natural numbers. By the Löwenheim Skolem Theorem it follows that A also has uncountable models. How can this be reconciled with the common assertion that Peano's axioms uniquely characterize the natural numbers? The answer appears to lie in the fact that Peano's Induction Axiom cannot be expressed fully in any language L. One statement of this axiom would equate it with the scheme

$$[P(0) \wedge \mathsf{A}x[P(x) \supset P(x+1)] \supset \mathsf{A}xP(x),$$

for all properties P. Its intuitive content is that the domain contains no elements beyond the set N of those obtainable from 0 by successive addition of 1. To express this in L, we have to replace $P(x)$ by $p(x)$, for $p(x)$ restricted to be a formula of L. But this restricts the properties P to those expressible in L. We conclude that, however L is chosen, we cannot express in L properties agreeing precisely with all our intuitions, and, in particular, we cannot express the property of belonging to N.

For an example of the second kind, we want a theory, phrased in a language of low cardinality, which is supposed to assure the existence of a large number of objects. One of the more modest formulations of set theory will do. For definiteness we suppose that L is countable and contains no function symbols, and only a single binary relation symbol ϵ, with the intention that $x \epsilon y$ means x is a member of the set y. Among the axioms for our theory T we suppose that there is one assuring that every model contains a countable set, and one asserting that, for any set x, there exists a set $\sigma(x)$ whose members are just the subsets of x. On the surface of it, any model for T must contain a countable set x and with it an uncountable set $\sigma(x)$. However, the Löwenheim Skolem Theorem tells us that T has a countable model. Here we must conclude that, again, certain expressions in the language do not receive their intended intuitive meaning in the model. There is ordinarily no difficulty in adjusting the model so that the symbol ϵ has the intended meaning. However, it cannot be assured that $\sigma(x)$ contain all subsets of x, but only those whose existence is demonstrable in T; thus $\sigma(x)$ remains countable. The usual proof that $\sigma(x)$ has a larger cardinal than x goes through, but shows only that there exists in the model no map from x onto $\sigma(x)$. Altogether we see that the concept of cardinality is relative; even if theory and metatheory are based on the same axioms, they need not attribute the same cardinality to an element of the model.

CATEGORICITY

A theory is called *categorical* if it admits essentially just one model, that is, if it is consistent and if any two models are in the obvious sense isomorphic. If one assumes that the concepts of property and set have an unambiguous meaning, say within an agreed metatheory, and one restricts attention to interpretations in which these concepts receive the prescribed meaning, then the usual sets of axioms for the natural numbers, the rational numbers, or the real numbers are categorical. However, if we consider axiomatic theories in the present sense, as the set T of all consequences of some set A of axioms, the Löwenheim Skolem Theorem implies that no theory that has an infinite model can be categorical.

A reasonable substitute for categoricity is the weaker concept of categoricity in power. A set P of formulas in a language L with identity symbol is *categorical in the power*, or cardinal, m iff, within isomorphism, it has exactly one model of cardinal m. The following criterion for completeness is due to Vaught.

> THEOREM. Let a theory T, defined by a set A of axioms of cardinal no greater than m, be categorical in power m, where m is infinite and admit no finite model. Then T is complete.

To prove this, suppose T not complete, and hence that, for some sentence p, neither p nor $\neg p$ belongs to T. Both the sets $A \cup \{p\}$ and $A \cup \{\neg p\}$ are then consistent, and, by the Löwenheim Skolem Theorem, both admit models, M_1 and M_2, of cardinal m. The assumption that A is categorical in power m implies that M_1 and M_2 are isomorphic. But this contradicts the fact that p holds in M_1 but not in M_2

The proof would go through if we replaced categoricity in power m by the weaker assumption that any two models of cardinal m are *elementarily equivalent* in the sense that they satisfy exactly the same sentences of L. However, this is of little advantage for the applications.

We have already seen that the theory of dense linear order is complete. This could also be deduced from a theorem of Cantor (which is not difficult to prove using the Axiom of Choice) that this theory is categorical in the first infinite cardinal $\aleph_0$, that is, any two dense linearly ordered countable sets are isomorphic.

It follows from Tarski's decision method for real arithmetic that the theory T, in a language L whose special symbols are $=$, $+$, and $\times$, of the field of all algebraic numbers is complete. This can also be obtained from Vaught's Theorem in the following way. First, it is easy to see that the models for T are precisely the algebraically closed fields of characteristic zero. Next, such a field F is determined up to isomorphism by its transcendence degree d, that is, the (uniquely determined) cardinal of a maximal set of algebraically independent elements from F. If d is finite or countable, then F is countable; otherwise F has cardinal d. It follows that T is categorical in every uncountable infinite cardinal m, whence T is complete. It is worth noting that the complete theory T is not categorical in the countable cardinal $\aleph_0$: the field of algebraic numbers and the field of all algebraic functions are both countable models for T, but clearly not isomorphic.

For further discussion of these matters see Robinson.

GENTZEN'S NATURAL INFERENCE

We turn now to Gentzen's axiomatization of the predicate logic. For convenience we now suppose that L has connectives N, C, D, A, and E, together with a countable set of variables, a countable set R of relation symbols, and no function symbols. It will be convenient also to use different symbols for the free and bound variables. We suppose the variables divided into two sets, $V = (v_1, v_2, \ldots)$ and $\Omega = (\omega_1, \omega_2, \ldots)$, and admit as well formed only thos formulas in which every free variable comes from the set V and every bound variable from the set Ω. The chief advantage of this arrangement is that we can now always substitute in any formula a variable from the set V.

The axiomatization we shall describe constitutes a slight extension of the concept of axiomatization as introduced earlier. Instead of single formulas we shall deal with finite sets of formulas, and, indeed, with ordered pairs of such sets. If S and T are any finite sets of formulas, we shall call the ordered pair $C = (S, T)$ a *sequent*, and shall use for C the more suggestive notation $S \rightarrow T$. We shall also write $S_1, S_2 \rightarrow T_1, T_2$ instead of $S_1 \cup S_2 \rightarrow T_1 \cup T_2$. A sequent C: $S \rightarrow T$ is *valid*, where $S = (s_1, \ldots, s_m)$ and $T = (t_1, \ldots, t_n)$, iff the formula $\bigwedge s_i \supset \bigvee t_j$ is valid. This should make clear the intended meaning of a sequent, as asserting that, under joint assumption of all the premises s_i, some one of the alternative conclusions t_j follows.

We shall specify certain sequents as axioms, together with certain rules of inference for sequents, thereby obtaining a definition of a proof of a sequent. Our aim is now an Adequacy Theorem, to the effect that a (well formed) sequent is valid iff it has a proof.

An *axiom* is a sequent C: $S \to T$ such that S and T have a formula in common.

The *rules of inference* are relations between a premise C, or a pair of premises C_1 and C_2, and a conclusion D. We shall exhibit the schemes for the rules of inference in the form

$$\frac{C}{D} \quad \text{or} \quad \frac{C_1 \mid C_2}{D}.$$

At times it will be convenient to treat a one-premise rule as a two-premise rule with two identical premises. Each rule of inference consists of all pairs, or triples, of well-formed formulas conforming to a certain scheme; the schemes are as follows.

$$N- \quad \frac{S \to T,\ p}{S,\ \neg p \to T} \qquad N+ \quad \frac{S, p \to T}{S, \to T,\ \neg p}$$

$$C- \quad \frac{S,\ p,\ q \to T}{S,\ p \wedge q \to T} \qquad C+ \quad \frac{S \to T,\ p \mid S \to T,\ q}{S \to T,\ p \wedge q}$$

$$D- \quad \frac{S,\ p \to T \mid S,\ q \to T}{S,\ p \vee q \to T} \qquad D+ \quad \frac{S \to T,\ p,\ q}{S \to T,\ p \vee q}$$

$$A- \quad \frac{S,\ p(x) \to T}{S,\ \mathsf{A}\xi p(\xi) \to T} \qquad A+ \quad \frac{S \to T,\ p(x)}{S \to T,\ \mathsf{A}\xi p(\xi)}$$

$$E- \quad \frac{S,\ p(x) \to T}{S,\ \mathsf{E}\xi p(\xi) \to T} \qquad E+ \quad \frac{S \to T,\ p(x)}{S \to T,\ \mathsf{E}\xi p(\xi)}$$

In connection with schemes $A+$ and $E-$ it is required that x not occur in S or T.

A *derivation* from a set W of sequents to a sequent D is a finite series $C_1, \ldots, C_n$ of sequents such that $C_n = D$ and that each C_i is an axiom, a member of W, or is the conclusion, under one of the rules, of an inference whose premises occur earlier in the series. A *proof* of D is a derivation of D from the empty set of premises. A sequent D is a *theorem* iff there exists a proof of D.

It is easy to see that every axiom is valid, and that if the premises of an inference are valid, then the conclusion also is valid. It follows that every theorem is valid, and it remains to prove the converse.

It is also easy to see that it is decidable whether a given sequent is an axiom, and whether a given sequent follows from two others by a rule of inference. Thus it is decidable whether a given series of sequents constitutes a derivation from given W to given D.

Before giving an example of a proof, we remark that in this axiomatization, in contrast with that discussed earlier, the burden has been shifted from the axioms, which are here utterly trivial, to the rules of inference, which are here relatively numerous. Each individual rule, however, is very simple, serves a very specific purpose, and is obviously just the right rule for this purpose. For example, the rule $D-$ provides the only way of introducing the connective $\vee$ into the left member of a sequent, in the course of a derivation, and this rule describes exactly the circumstances under which such an introduction is justified. In this sense, the two rules $D-$ and $D+$ together fulfil the specific role of giving a behavioristic characterization of the connective $\vee$. This specialization of the rules leaves us very little choice of premises from which to derive a given conclusion, and hence very nearly determines the shape of the proof of a given theorem.

As an illustration, we give a proof of the sequent

$$\mathsf{A}\xi\mathsf{E}\eta r\xi\eta \rightarrow \mathsf{A}\xi\mathsf{E}\eta\mathsf{E}\zeta(r\xi\eta \wedge r\eta\zeta),$$

where r is a binary relation symbol. In the proof, which follows, justification for each line is indicated in the right margin.

$$rxy,\ ryz \rightarrow rxy \quad \Big| \quad rxy,\ ryz \rightarrow ryz \qquad \text{(axioms)}$$

$$rxy,\ ryz \rightarrow rxy \wedge ryz \qquad (C+)$$

$$rxy,\ ryz \rightarrow \mathsf{E}\zeta(rxy \wedge ry\zeta) \qquad (E+)$$

$$rxy,\ ryz \rightarrow \mathsf{E}\eta\mathsf{E}\zeta(rx\eta \wedge r\eta\zeta) \qquad (E+)$$

$$rxy,\ \mathsf{E}\eta ry\eta \rightarrow \mathsf{E}\eta\mathsf{E}\zeta(rx\eta \wedge r\eta\zeta) \qquad (E-)$$

$$rxy,\ \mathsf{A}\xi\mathsf{E}\eta r\xi\eta \rightarrow \mathsf{E}\eta\mathsf{E}\zeta(rx\eta \wedge r\eta\zeta) \qquad (A-)$$

$$\mathsf{E}\eta rx\eta,\ \mathsf{A}\xi\mathsf{E}\eta r\xi\eta \rightarrow \mathsf{E}\eta\mathsf{E}\zeta(rx\eta \wedge r\eta\zeta) \qquad (E-)$$

$$\mathsf{A}\xi\mathsf{E}\eta r\xi\eta,\ \mathsf{A}\xi\mathsf{E}\eta r\xi\eta \rightarrow \mathsf{E}\eta\mathsf{E}\zeta(rx\eta \wedge r\eta\zeta) \qquad (A-)$$

$$\mathsf{A}\xi\mathsf{E}\eta r\xi\eta,\ \mathsf{A}\xi\mathsf{E}\eta r\xi\eta \rightarrow \mathsf{A}\xi\mathsf{E}\eta\mathsf{E}\zeta(r\xi\eta \wedge r\eta\zeta) \qquad (A+)$$

It must be verified, of course, that the rules $A+$ and $E-$ have been used to replace a variable in a formula by a bound variable only when this variable occurs in no other formula of the sequent. This condition dictates, to a large extent, the order of the steps in the proof. It must also be observed that the last sequent is indeed the sequent $S \rightarrow T$ to be proved; for S is not altered by listing its sole member twice. It is primarily this possibility, of coalescence of multiple occurrences of a formula, which makes the construction of a proof for a given valid sequent not an entirely mechanical matter.

EXERCISES.

1. How can the proof above be altered without making it longer?

2. Prove the sequent $p \wedge (q \vee r) \rightarrow (p \wedge q) \vee (p \wedge r)$; the sequent $\mathsf{E}\xi\mathsf{A}\eta p \rightarrow \mathsf{A}\eta\,\mathsf{E}\xi p$.

3. Adapt the formalism above to the case that L contains the additional connectives 0 and 1; that L contains J; that L contains function symbols.

SECOND FORMULATION

By the rule $N+$ we can transpose all formulas from left to right, replacing each sequent C: $s_1, \ldots, s_m \rightarrow t_1, \ldots, t_n$ by an equivalent sequent C': $\varnothing \rightarrow \neg s_1, \ldots, \neg s_m, t_1, \ldots, t_n$. It will simplify the exposition to treat only sequents of this form, $\varnothing \rightarrow T$, and we accordingly reformulate the whole theory by uniformly transposing every sequent to this form. The first two symbols in the notation $\varnothing \rightarrow T$ now become superfluous, and we define a *sequent* to be simply a finite set T of formulas.

An *axiom* is now a sequent T that contains some formula p together with its negation $\neg p$.

The literal translations of the schemes of inference are as follows:

$$N- \quad \frac{T,\ p}{T,\ \neg\neg p} \qquad N+ \quad \frac{T,\ \neg p}{T,\ \neg p}$$

$$C- \quad \frac{T,\ \neg p,\ \neg q}{T,\ \neg(p \wedge q)} \qquad C+ \quad \frac{T,\ p \mid T,\ q}{T,\ p \wedge q}$$

$$D- \quad \frac{T,\ \neg p \mid T,\ \neg q}{T,\ \neg(p \vee q)} \qquad D+ \quad \frac{T,\ p,\ q}{T,\ p \vee q}$$

$$A- \quad \frac{T,\ \neg p(x)}{T,\ \neg \mathsf{A}\xi p(\xi)} \qquad A+ \quad \frac{T,\ p(x)}{T,\ \mathsf{A}\xi p(\xi)}$$

$$E- \quad \frac{T,\ \neg p(x)}{T,\ \neg \mathsf{E}\xi p(\xi)} \qquad E+ \quad \frac{T,\ p(x)}{T,\ \mathsf{E}\xi p(\xi)}$$

Here, in $A+$ and $E-$, it is required that x not occur in T.

First, we drop the rule $N+$, which has become vacuous. Second, we replace $A-$ and $E+$ by the following two rules:

$$A-' \quad \frac{T,\ \mathrm{E}\xi \neg p(\xi)}{T,\ \neg \mathrm{A}\xi p(\xi)}, \qquad E-' \quad \frac{T,\ \mathrm{A}\xi \neg p(\xi)}{T,\ \neg \mathrm{E}\xi p(\xi)}.$$

Note that an application of $A-$ can always be effected by succesive applications of $E+$ and $A-'$, according to the scheme

$$\cfrac{\cfrac{T,\ \neg p(x)}{T,\ \mathrm{E}\xi \neg p(\xi)}\ (E_+)}{T,\ \neg \mathrm{A}\xi p(\xi)}\ (A_-)\ ;$$

and, in any derivation, it can be arranged that every use of $A-'$ occurs in such a context. It follows that replacing $A-$ by $A-'$ does not alter the set of theorems, nor, similarly, does replacement of $E-$ by $E-'$.

Moreover, to prove the adequacy of the first formulation it suffices to prove that of the second. For if C is any sequent in the first formulation, and C' the transposed sequent, it is easy to see how to translate any proof of C in the first formalism into a proof of C' in the second, and conversely.

EXERCISES

1. Give a full proof that replacing $A-$ and $E-$ by $A-'$ and $E-'$ does not alter the set of theorems.

2. Give detailed rules for transforming a proof in the first formalism into one in the second, and conversely.

3. Carry out the analog of the above, transposing now all formulas to the left instead of to the right.

THE ADEQUACY THEOREM

We shall modify the formulation of the Gentzen calculus once more, in order to arrange that no sequent can be obtained as conclusion under more than one rule of inference. It can be seen by inspection that this would be the case if, in a conclusion of the form $C = T \cup \{p\}$, we could always tell which formula p had just been introduced by the rule of inference. This we arrange by viewing each sequent C as an ordered set, and arranging that p is the first formula in C that could have been introduced by any rule.

Precisely, a *sequent* is now an ordered set $C = (c_1, \ldots, c_n)$ of formulas, with repetitions permitted. Again, an *axiom* is a sequent C containing both some formula p and also its negation $\neg p$. A formula is *simple* if it is either an atomic formula p or the negation $\neg p$ of an atomic formula p. A sequent C is *simple* if every formula in C is simple. The notation T, U, V or $T \cup U \cup V$ will mean the sequent obtained by combining T, U, and V in that order.

Each of our previous schemes had the form

$$\frac{T, U_1 \mid T, U_2}{T, U_3} ;$$

we now replace it by the corresponding scheme,

$$\frac{T, U_1, V \mid T, U_2, V}{T, U_3, V} ,$$

now with the requirement that T be simple. We introduce one further modification of the scheme $E+$, so that it now takes the form

$$E+ \qquad \frac{T,\ p(x),\ V,\ \mathsf{E}\xi p(\xi)}{T,\ \mathsf{E}\xi p(\xi),\ V}\ .$$

It is now evident that a sequent C can be the conclusion of an inference iff it is not simple. In this case, writing $C = T \cup U_3 \cup V$ where U_3 is the first non-simple formula in C, we can determine the rule of inference uniquely by inspection of U_3. Indeed, the premises of the inference are uniquely determined except in case of the rules $A+$ and $E+$, where the variable x in the premise is not fully determined.

We now start from a given sequent S, and supply premises S_1 and S_2 for S if this is both necessary and possible, and, continuing thus, whenever any sequent T arises, supplying premises T_1 and T_2 for T if this is both necessary and possible. More precisely, if a given T is either an axiom or simple, we supply no premises for T, and otherwise we supply one or two premises for T. These premises for T are uniquely determined except in the case of rules $A+$ and $E+$. In the case of $A+$, where T has the form $U \cup \mathsf{A}\xi p(\xi) \cup V$, we chose the premise T_1 to be $U \cup p(x) \cup V$ where x is the first of $v_1, v_2, \ldots$ that does not occur in U or V. In the case of $E+$, where T has the form $U \cup \mathsf{E}\xi p(\xi) \cup V$, in $T_1 = U \cup p(x) \cup V \cup \mathsf{E}\xi p(\lambda)$, we take x to be the first v_i such that $p(x)$ does not already occur as a formula in any sequent in the chain of conclusions leading downward from T to S. The tree $T(S)$ is the smallest set of sequents containing S and such that, whenever any sequent T belongs to $T(S)$, then so do the premises associated with T according to the above rules.

A sequent D in $T(S)$ is a *top* if no other sequent stands above it as premise. From the definition of $T(S)$, a top must be either an axiom or simple. If $T(S)$ is finite and all its tops are axioms, then, disregarding the order on the members of a sequent, $T(S)$ yields directly a proof of S, as unordered sequent, in the second formulation. To complete the proof of the Adequacy Theorem we must show in the remaining case, where either $T(S)$ is infinite or has a top that is not an axiom, that S is not valid.

If some top D in $T(S)$ is not an axiom, clearly $T(S)$ contains a chain $S = S_1, S_2, \ldots, S_d = D$ in which each S_{n+1} is one of the premises for S_n. If $T(S)$ is infinite, we show that $T(S)$ contains an infinite chain $S = S_1, S_2, \ldots,$ in which each S_{n+1} is one of the premises for S_n. By hypothesis, there are infinitely many sequents in $T(S)$ standing above $S_1 = S;$ supposing inductively that we have chosen $S_1, \ldots, S_n$ so that there are infinitely many sequents above S_n, then clearly the same is true for at least one of the premises for S_n, and we have only to choose such a premise as S_{n+1}. [In case both premises for S_n have this property, we can avoid the Axiom of Choice by choosing always the earlier according to a prescribed alphabetical order on the symbols of L.] In either case, we denote by P the set of all formulas that occur in some sequent S_n of the chain.

We now define an interpretation ϕ of L with domain $\mathsf{V} = (v_1, v_2, \ldots)$. For a variable x in V we define $\phi x = x;$ it is immaterial how we interpret the variables ξ in Ω, and for simplicity we take $\phi\omega_i = v_i$. For a relation symbol r in R_n we define ϕr by specifying that $(\phi r)(x_1, \ldots, x_n) = 1$ iff the formula $rx_1 \ldots x_n$ does *not* belong to P. We shall show, by induction on length, that p in P implies $\phi p = 0$.

If $p = rx_1 \ldots x_n$ is an atomic formula, and p is in P, then $\phi p = (\phi r)(x_1, \ldots, x_n) = 0$ by the definition of ϕr. We next suppose that $p = \neg q$ where $q = rx_1 \ldots x_n$ is an atomic formula, and that p is in P. If also q were in P, we should have p in some S_n and q in some S_m, whence both would be in S_k for $k = \text{Max}(n, m)$. Then S_k would be an axiom, which is clearly impossible for any member of our chain. We conclude that q is not in P, whence it follows from the definition of ϕr that $\phi q = (\phi r)(x_1, \ldots, x_n) = 1$ and thus $\phi p = 0$. This establishes the conclusion in the case that p is simple.

Suppose next that p is not simple, but not of the form $p = \mathsf{E}\xi q(\xi)$. Now $p = U_3$ in the conclusion S_n of some inference of the form

$$\frac{T,\, U_1,\, V \mid T,\, U_2,\, V}{T,\, U_3,\, V}$$

and it can be seen by inspection in each case that $\phi U_3 = 1$ implies $\phi U_1 = \phi U_2 = 1$. Now one of the formulas U_1 and U_2 belongs to

S_{n+1} and so to P, and this formula q is shorter than p. By the induction hypothesis, $\phi q = 0$, that is, either $\phi U_1 = 0$ or $\phi U_2 = 0$, whence it follows that $\phi p = \phi U_3 = 0$.

Suppose finally that $p = \mathsf{E}\xi q(\xi)$ occurs in $S_n = T \cup \mathsf{E}\xi q(\xi) \cup V$. Then it is clear from the rules that p occurs also in each S_m coming after S_n in the chain. If some $S_m = T_m \cup \{p\} \cup V_m$, and T_m is not simple, then $S_{m+1} = T_{m+1} \cup \{p\} \cup V_{m+1}$ where the sum of the lengths of the non-simple formulas in T_{m+1} is smaller than in T_m. If T_m is simple, then $S_{m+1} = T_m \cup \{q(v_i)\} \cup V_m \cup \{p\}$, where v_i is the first variable such that $q(v_i)$ does not occur in any earlier member of the chain. From this it follows that the chain contains infinitely many sequents S_m with T_m simple, and that $q(v_i)$, for each v_i, will ultimately appear in some member of the chain. Thus $q(x)$ is in P for every x in V. Since $q(x)$ is shorter than $p = \mathsf{E}\xi q(\xi)$, it follows from the induction hypothesis that $\phi q(x) = 0$ for all x in V, and from this it follows that $\phi p = 0$.

We have now shown that p in P implies $\phi p = 0$. Since every s in $S = S_1$ belongs to P, we have $\phi s = 0$ for every such s, and it follows that S is not valid. In all, we have shown that if S is not a theorem, then S is not valid. This completes the proof of the Adequacy Theorem.

ADEQUACY THEOREM. For every sequent S, S is a theorem iff S is valid.

The construction of the tree $T(S)$ provides us with a method for either finding a proof of S or constructing an infinite counter example. It does not provide a decision method since, for general S, we can prescribe no point in the construction of $T(S)$ upward from S where, if we have not already a proof, we can be sure that we will never find one. However, the method, which is essentially due to Herbrand, provides a procedure that is not only natural but reasonably efficient for looking for a proof, and it has been suggested as a means for testing the truth of mathematical sentences on a computing machine. It is also possible to find limited, but by no means entirely uninteresting, classes of sequents S for which the method can be guaranteed to give a decision.

THE HERBRAND GENTZEN THEOREM

A refinement of the earlier ideas of Herbrand is given by a theorem of Gentzen, now commonly called the Herbrand Gentzen Theorem.

A formula is *prenex* if all occurrences of quantifiers precede all occurrences of the other connectives. More explicitly, a prenex formula has the form $p = Q_1\xi_1 \ldots Q_n\xi_n q$ where each Q_i is either A or E, and where q is a formula that does not contain A or E. A sequent is *prenex* if all its formulas are prenex.

PROPOSITION. Every formula is equivalent to a prenex formula.

This can be proved directly by induction of the length of a formula, using the following rules:

$$\neg \mathsf{A}\xi p \models\!\dashv \mathsf{E}\xi \neg p, \quad \neg \mathsf{E}\xi p \models\!\dashv \mathsf{A}\xi \neg p,$$

$$p \wedge \mathsf{A}\xi q(\xi) \models\!\dashv \mathsf{A}\zeta(p \wedge q(\zeta)), \quad p \wedge \mathsf{E}\xi q(\xi) \models\!\dashv \mathsf{E}\zeta(p \wedge q(\zeta)),$$

$$p \vee \mathsf{A}\xi q(\xi) \models\!\dashv \mathsf{A}\zeta(p \vee q(\zeta)), \quad p \vee \mathsf{E}\xi q(\xi) \models\!\dashv \mathsf{E}\zeta(p \vee q(\zeta)),$$

where ζ is a new variable.

HERBRAND GENTZEN THEOREM. If S is a valid prenex sequent, then there exists a valid sequent P that contains no quantifiers, and a derivation from P to S by the quantifier rules $A-$, $A+$, $E\neg$, and $E+$ alone.

In stating the theorem we had in mind the first formulation, but it is easy to see that it suffices to prove it for the second formulation. Let C: $s_1, \ldots, s_m \rightarrow t_1, \ldots, t_n$ be any prenex sequent in the first formulation. For each s_i, let $*s_i$ be the prenex formula obtained from $\neg s_i$ by successively replacing a part $\neg \mathsf{A}\xi$ by $\mathsf{E}\xi\neg$ or $\neg \mathsf{E}\xi$ by $\mathsf{A}\xi\neg$. Let $C' = (*s_1, \ldots, *s_m, t_1, \ldots, t_n)$. Suppose now prenex S given, and a derivation in the second formulation, by quantifier rules alone, of S' from some quantifier free D'. Then a derivation in the first formulation of S from some quantifier free D, by quantifier rules alone, is easily obtained. Appropriate formulas $*s_i$ are carried back into formulas s_i on the left, and applications of rules $A+$ and $E+$ to such $*s_i$ are replaced by applications of rules $E-$ and $A-$ to the corresponding s_i.

It remains to prove the Herbrand Gentzen Theorem for the second formulation. For this purpose it is convenient to introduce a new rule X, given by the scheme $\dfrac{T}{T, U}$. Evidently this change does not affect the content of either the Adequacy Theorem or the Herbrand Gentzen Theorem. Under the new rule X, every axiom can be obtained as the conclusion of an inference with a single premise of the form $C = (p, \neg p)$. Therefore we shall lose nothing in henceforth requiring the axioms to be of this special form.

Suppose now that S is a valid prenex sequent in the second formulation. By the Adequacy Theorem, since S is valid, there exists a proof D of S. By hypothesis, S is prenex. Moreover, if the conclusion of an inference is prenex, then evidently both premises are prenex. We conclude that every formula in the proof D is prenex. In particular, it follows that D can contain no inference by the rules $A-'$ and $E-'$. Further, if an axiom $C = (p, \neg p)$ occurs in D, from the fact that $\neg p$ is prenex we conclude that p contains no quantifiers, and therefore that C contains no quantifiers. If we could show that, in D, all the propositional inferences, by rules X, $N-$, $C-$, $C+$, $D-$, and $D+$, occurred at the top, leading from the axioms to a sequent P, which contained no quantifiers, and that the remainder of D consisted of a derivation from P to S by the rules $A+$ and $E+$ alone, we would be done. Indeed, it will suffice to show that we can choose D so that all applications of $A+$ and $E+$ occur consecutively at the end of the proof; for if P contained a prenex formula $p = Q_1\xi_1 \ldots Q_n\xi_n q(\xi_1, \ldots, \xi_n)$, necessarily as the result of rule X, we could modify P to P' by introducing some $q(x_1, \ldots, x_n)$ instead of p, and then passing from P' to P by use of $A+$ and $E+$.

By an obvious induction on the length of a proof, it will suffice to suppose that D ends with a propositional inference, one of whose premises is obtained by a quantificational inference, and to show that these last two inferences can be replaced by a derivation in which all propositional inferences precede all quantificational inferences. We may suppose then that D ends with a propositional inference

$$\frac{T, q_1 \mid T, q_2}{T, q}$$

where the two premises may coincide, and where q_1 and q_2 may be missing if the rule is X. We may suppose further that the sequent T, q_1 is the conclusion of an inference by $A+$ or $E+$. Since q_1 is prenex, the formula $Q\xi p(\xi)$ introduced by this inference must belong to T. Thus the derivation under consideration has the following form:

$$\frac{\dfrac{U, p(x), q_1}{U, Q\xi p(\xi), q_1} \mid U, Q\xi p(\xi), q_2}{U, Q\xi p(\xi), q} .$$

In case the upper inference is by rule $A+$, the variable x cannot occur in U or in q_1. By relettering the part of the proof leading to the sequent $U, Q\xi p(\xi), q_1$ we can arrange that x does not occur in q.

We now replace the derivation under consideration by the following:

$$\frac{\dfrac{\dfrac{U, p(x), q_1}{U, Q\xi p(\xi), p(x), q_1} \mid \dfrac{U, Q\xi p(\xi), q_2}{U, Q\xi p(\xi), p(x), q_2}}{U, Q\xi p(\xi), p(x), q}}{U, Q\xi p(\xi), q}$$

Here the two upper inferences are by rule X. The next inference is by the same propositional rule as gave the last step in D. The final inference is by the same rule $A+$ or $E+$ as occurred in the original derivation. If this last inference is by rule $A+$, it must be checked that the variable x does not occur in U, $Q\xi p(\xi)$, or in q. Now, from the use of the rule $A+$ in the original derivation we conclude that x does not occur in U. From the definition of $Q\xi p(\xi)$ in terms of $p(x)$ it is clear that x does not occur in $Q\xi p(\xi)$. Finally, by our preliminary relettering of the proof D we have ensured that x does not occur in q. Since this new derivation clearly has the required properties, the proof of the Herbrand Gentzen Theorem is complete.

EXERCISE. Adapt the proof of the Herbrand Gentzen Theorem to a language L with the additional connectives 0, 1; to a language L with function symbols.

CRAIG'S THEOREM

We illustrate the usefulness of the Herbrand Gentzen Theorem by using it to prove a theorem of Craig, for which, despite its intuitively obvious nature, no essentially different syntactical proof is known. For simplicity we now assume that L contains the connectives 0 and 1.

CRAIG'S THEOREM. Let p and q be formulas such that $p \models q$. Then $p \models m$ and $m \models q$ for some formula m which contains only those relation symbols that occur in both p and q.

We treat first the case that neither p nor q contains quantifiers. We may suppose that p is in disjunctive form, $p = \bigvee_i \bigwedge_j p_{ij}$ where p_{ij} is simple, and that $q = \neg r$ for some r in disjunctive form, $r = \bigvee_h \bigwedge_k r_{hk}$ where each r_{hk} is simple. Let $m = \bigvee_i \bigwedge_j' p_{ij}$ be the formula obtained from p by deleting each p_{ij} which contains a relation symbol that does not occur in q. Clearly $p \models m$, and m contains only relation symbols that occur in both p and q. It remains to show that $m \models q$. Now $p \models q$ implies that $p, r \models 0$, whence it follows that for each pair i and h, $\wedge_j p_{ij}, \wedge_k r_{hk} \models 0$, that is, that some $p_{ij}, r_{hk} \models 0$. This last is possible only if p_{ij} contains the same relation symbol as r_{hk}, hence if p_{ij} remains in the part $\wedge'_j p_{ij}$ of m. It follows that $\wedge'_j p_{ij}, \wedge_k r_{hk} \models 0$, whence m, $r \models 0$, and $m \models q$.

To pass to the general case we need a lemma.

LEMMA. Suppose there exists a derivation by quantificational rules alone from a sequent $S \rightarrow T$ to a sequent $S' \rightarrow T'$, and let m be an arbitrary formula. Then, for some formula m', there exists a derivation by quantificational rules from $S \rightarrow m$ to $S' \rightarrow m'$, and another from $m \rightarrow T$ to $m' \rightarrow T'$.

Arguing by induction on the length of the given derivation from $S \rightarrow T$ to $S' \rightarrow T'$, we may suppose that this derivation consists of a single step, by one of the rules $A-$, $A+$, $E-$, $E+$. If the given rule is $A-$ or $E+$, with no condition on the occurrence of variables, we may take $m' = m$. Then one of the two derivations

$$\frac{S \rightarrow m}{S' \rightarrow m}, \quad \frac{m \rightarrow T}{m \rightarrow T'}$$

is trivial, while the other is justified by the same rule $A-$ or $E+$. If the given rule is $A+$, then the given inference has the form

$$\frac{S \rightarrow U,\ p(x)}{S \rightarrow U,\ \mathsf{A}\xi p(\xi)}$$

where x does not occur in S or in U. Now x may occur in m, which we write in any case as $m = m(x)$, and we take $m' = \mathsf{A}\eta m(\eta)$, where η is a variable that does not occur in $m(x)$. We now justify the two following derivations,

$$\frac{S \rightarrow m(x)}{S \rightarrow \mathsf{A}\eta m(\eta)}, \quad \cfrac{\cfrac{m(x) \rightarrow U,\ p(x)}{\mathsf{A}\eta m(\eta) \rightarrow U,\ p(x)}}{\mathsf{A}\eta m(\eta) \rightarrow U,\ \mathsf{A}\xi p(\xi)},$$

the first by $A+$, since x does not occur in S, and the second by $A-$ followed by $A+$, since x does not occur in $\mathsf{A}\eta m(\eta)$ or in U. The case that the given rule is $E-$ is entirely analogous.

To complete the proof of Craig's Theorem, we suppose given p and q such that $p \models q$. Without loss of generality we may suppose that p and q are prenex, and hence that $p \rightarrow q$ is a valid prenex sequent. By the Herbrand Gentzen Theorem, there exists a derivation of $p \rightarrow q$, by quantificational rules only, from a valid sequent $S \rightarrow T$ that contains no quantifiers. Let $S = (s_1, \ldots, s_m)$ and $T = (t_1, \ldots, t_n)$. By Craig's Theorem for formulas without quantifiers, which we have already established, there exists a formula m such that $\bigwedge s_i \models m$, that $m \models \bigvee t_j$, and that m contains only relational symbols that occur in both S and T. By the lemma, there exists a formula m' and derivations, by quantifier rules alone, from $S \rightarrow m$ to $p \rightarrow m'$ and from $m \rightarrow T$ to $m' \rightarrow q$. From the choice of m it follows that the two sequents $S \rightarrow m$ and $m \rightarrow T$ are valid, whence it follows that the two sequents $p \rightarrow m'$ and $m' \rightarrow q$ derived from them are also valid. Thus $p \models m'$ and $m \models q'$. Finally, since the derivation from $S \rightarrow m$ to $p \rightarrow m$ and that from $m \rightarrow T$ to $m \rightarrow q$ are by quantifier rules alone, p, m', and q, respectively, contain exactly the same relational symbols as S, m, and T. It follows that m' contains no relational symbol that does not occur in both p and q.

EXERCISES

1. An occurrence of a symbol in a formula is called positive or negative according as the number of subformulas beginning with N and containing the occurrence is even or odd. Show that Craig's Theorem can be strengthened to require that a relation symbol occur positively in m only if it occurs positively in both p and q, and similarly for negative occurrences.

2. Show that a formula $p = p(r)$ is equivalent to one with only positive occurrences of the relation symbol r of rank n iff p is increasing in r, in the sense that $\mathsf{A}\xi_1 \ldots \mathsf{A}\xi_n(r\xi_1 \ldots \xi_n \supset r'\xi_1 \ldots \xi_n) \models p(r) \supset p(r')$.

3. Observe that if $\equiv$ is a congruence on an algebra A, then $\mathsf{A}\xi\mathsf{A}\eta(\xi = \eta \supset \xi \equiv \eta)$ holds. Deduce the *Homomorphism Theorem,* that a formula p, in a language L with $=$ and function symbols but no other relation symbols, is equivalent to a formula with only positive occurrences of $=$ iff whenever p holds for an algebra A it holds also for every quotient algebra $[A]$.

DIAGONAL ARGUMENTS AND THE PARADOXES

The heart of Gödel's proof of the incompleteness of arithmetic is a *diagonal argument.* Before giving a sketch of Gödel's argument, we say something about diagonal arguments.

The most modest and familiar use of a diagonal argument is in Cantor's proof that the set of real numbers is not countable. It is shown that no list, $r_1, r_2, \ldots$ of real numbers (indexed by the positive integers) can contain every real number. Given such a list, for each positive integer i define $a_i = 7$ if the i-th digit to the right of the point in the decimal expansion of r_i is not a 7, and $a_i = 4$ if this digit is a 7. Then the number with decimal expansion $0.a_1a_2\ldots$ is different from all the numbers r_i on the list.

The same argument in a broader context gives Cantor's theorem that the set T of all subsets of a set S has a greater cardinal than S. We must show that no map f from S into T maps S onto all of T. Given f, define U to be the set of all s in S such that s is not in $f(s)$. Then U is not $f(u)$ for any u in S, since we have u in U iff u not in $f(u)$.

If we permit ourselves to apply this to a universal set S, containing everything, we arrive at a set T even larger than S, a contradiction. Russell's paradox is a simpler form of this argument. Define U to be the set of all sets X such that X is not a member of X. Then U is a member of U iff U is not a member of U.

Russell's paradox is the simplest of the mathematical paradoxes of set theory. Its discovery made clear that we must curtail the modes of reasoning by which it was obtained, and lent strong support to the demand that mathematicians examine their logical presuppositions more closely. Although most mathematicians, who are not inclined to use extravagant arguments, feel safe enough from the paradoxes, there have been given several exact formulations of the foundations of mathematics which are commonly believed to be free from contradiction. Unfortunately, as we shall see presently, we cannot hope to realize Hilbert's goal of showing unconditionally that any such theory is free from contradiction.

The earliest paradoxes are semantic rather than mathematical. One version of the Liar Paradox has Epimenides say: *I am lying*. Epimenides is lying iff he is not lying. The difficulty here lies not in mathematics but in the use of language. It has been pointed out correctly that the difficulty arises from self-reference: Epimenides' sentence refers implicitly to itself. But merely to denounce self-reference is not enough; as with the theory of sets, we must look for an exact theory of language in which the contradiction can no longer arise.

It is easier to consider the Liar Paradox in a modified form: *This sentence is false*. It might appear that the self-reference contained in the demonstrative *this* could not be made precise, but this is not the case. By an ingenious use of a diagonal argument Gödel has shown how, if we accept a formula p of a language L as expressing a property of sentences of L, it is possible to construct a sentence s expressing that this sentence s itself has the property P. The difficulty, as Tarski has shown, lies with the word *false*. In a language L we cannot reasonably suppose there is any formula p which expresses the property of sentences of L that they be true, or false.

The core of Gödel's argument lies in replacing the word *false* by the word *unprovable: This sentence is unprovable*. In a reasonable language the concept of provability for its own formulas is expressible, and a sentence s can be formulated asserting its own unprovability. The sentence is true iff it is not provable. Assuming that every provable sentence is true, we are led to the conclusion that the sentence s is true but not provable.

GÖDEL NUMBERS

For Gödel's argument we need a language L that can talk about itself, or at least a faithful replica of itself. Gödel's solution consists in translating L into a numerical code in such a way that all relevant syntactical properties of expressions correspond to reasonably elementary arithmetical properties of their code numbers. The language L must then contain enough notation to express these properties, and we must assume in L enough axioms to ensure that these expressions have the intended significance in any model.

If we are to attach distinct natural numbers to the symbols of L, the set of these symbols must be countable. Besides the connectives and an infinite set of variables, if we want to discuss arithmetic in L it is convenient to have symbols $=, +, \times, \overline{0}, \overline{1}$ for equality, addition, multiplication, zero, and one. It will be convenient to suppose that L has also a finite set $\mathsf{F} = (f_1, \ldots, f_\mathrm{f})$ of function symbols and a finite set $\mathsf{R} = (r_1, \ldots, r_\mathrm{r})$ of relation symbols. We shall think of the symbols of L ranged in the order

$$\mathsf{0}, \mathsf{1}, \mathsf{N}, \mathsf{C}, \mathsf{D}, \mathsf{A}, \mathsf{E}, =, +, \times, \overline{0}, \overline{1}, f_1, \ldots, f_\mathrm{f}, r_1, \ldots, r_\mathrm{r}, v_1, v_2, \ldots.$$

Let a be the function mapping this set in the given order onto the positive integers. We now define a function β attaching to each expression $\mathrm{e} = \mathrm{s}_1 \ldots \mathrm{s}_n$, where the s_i are symbols, the number

$$\beta[\mathrm{e}] = 2^{a[\mathrm{s}_1]} 3^{a[\mathrm{s}_2]} \ldots p_n^{a[\mathrm{s}_n]}$$

where $2, 3, \ldots, p_n$ are in order the first n primes. The essential thing about this function is that it assigns different numbers to different expressions, and that the numbers n and $a[\mathrm{s}_i]$ are easily computed from $\beta[\mathrm{e}]$. Since we shall want to talk about finite sequences $E = (\mathrm{e}_1, \ldots, \mathrm{e}_n)$ of expressions — for example, proofs — we repeat this device, defining a function γ of such sequences by setting

$$\gamma[E] = 2^{\beta[e_1]}3^{\beta[e_2]} \cdots p_n^{\beta[e_n]} .$$

We define $\gamma[e] = \gamma[E]$ for E with single member e, and $\gamma[s] = \gamma[e]$ for e with single symbol s. The numbers $\gamma[s]$, $\gamma[e]$, and $\gamma[s]$ are the *Gödel numbers* of s, e, and E.

EXPRESSIBILITY AND TARSKI'S THEOREM

We consider theories T in L defined by a set A of axioms that is decidable in the sense that it is decidable, for every formula p, whether p belongs to A. We require that A contain the set A_0 of axioms for predicate logic with identity, and also the set A_1 consisting of the following six axioms:

$$v_1 + \bar{0} = v_1, \qquad v_1 + (v_2 + \bar{1}) = (v_1 + v_2) + \bar{1},$$

$$v_1 \times \bar{0} = \bar{0}, \qquad v_1 \times (v_2 + \bar{1}) = (v_1 \times v_2) + v_1,$$

$$v_1 + \bar{1} \neq \bar{0}, \qquad v_1 + \bar{1} = v_2 + \bar{1} \supset v_1 = v_2.$$

We do not exclude that A contain further axioms. In particular, A may contain definitions fixing the interpretation of the remaining function and relation symbols in terms of that of $=$, $\bar{0}$, $\bar{1}$, $+$ and $\times$. For example, a pair of axioms $f(x, \bar{0}) = \bar{1}$, $f(x, y + \bar{1}) = f(x, y) \times x$ would serve as a *recursive definition*, imposing on the function symbol f the meaning $f(x, y) = x^y$.

Henceforth we shall use the word *true* to mean valid in the *standard model*, with domain the set N of natural numbers, and with the symbols $=$, $\bar{0}$, $\bar{1}$, $+$ and $\times$ receiving their customary meanings.

For each n in N, $n > 1$, we introduce the abbreviation $\bar{n} = (\ldots(\bar{1} + \bar{1}) + \ldots + \bar{1})$, n symbols $\bar{1}$. Let $\bar{N}$ be the set of terms $\bar{0}, \bar{1}, \bar{2}, \ldots$ in L. If ϕ is any model for T, it follows by induction from A_1, first, that the correspondence from n into $\phi\bar{n}$ carries

N one to one onto $\phi\bar{N}$, and, second, that it carries the operations $+$ and $\times$ on N into the operations $\phi(+)$ and $\phi(\times)$ on $\phi\bar{N}$. In view of this isomorphism we may identify $\phi\bar{N}$ with N without ambiguity, writing n for $\phi\bar{n}$, and $+$ and $\times$ instead of $\phi(+)$ and $\phi(\times)$.

A property $P(x_1, \ldots, x_n)$ of natural numbers will be called *expressible* in the theory T if there exists a formula $p = p(v_1, \ldots, v_n)$ in L such that, for all $m_1, \ldots, m_n$ in N, $P(m_1, \ldots, m_n)$ is true iff $p(\bar{m}_1, \ldots, \bar{m}_n)$ is true. A property P of symbols, expressions, and sequences of expressions is called expressible if the corresponding property of their Gödel numbers is expressible.

It should be clear on general principle that all of our syntactic concepts, such as variable, term, formula, and sentence, are expressible. For we can certainly express the corresponding condition on Gödel numbers in the ordinary notation of arithmetic, and to translate this into L we need only ensure that A contains recursive definitions of all arithmetical functions, such as x^y, that are used in such an expression. We have also assumed that the set A of axioms is decidable; when we finally come to give an exact definition of decidability, this will imply that the property of being an axiom is expressible. It is now clear that the property of being a proof, and indeed of E being a proof of a formula p, is expressible.

We may suppose then that L contains a particular formula $b(v_1, v_2)$ such that, for any two natural numbers m and n, $b(\bar{m}, \bar{n})$ is true iff m is the number of a proof of a formula whose number is n. Note then that the formula $\mathsf{E}v_2 b(v_2, v_1)$ expresses the property of being a theorem. We may also suppose that L contains a particular formula $s(v_1, v_2) = v_3$ such that $s(\bar{m}, \bar{n}) = \bar{q}$, for $m = \gamma[t]$ and $n = \gamma[p(v_1]$, is true iff $q = \gamma[p(\bar{m})]$.

With this machinery, we return to the Liar Paradox. Suppose that L contained, besides the formula $s(v_1, v_2) = v_3$ as above, a formula $w(v_1)$ expressing the property of a formula being true. Let $p(v_1) = \neg w(s(v_1, v_1))$, and let $m = \gamma[p(v_1)]$. Now $s(\bar{m}, \bar{m})$ is the number of the formula obtained by substituting the term $\bar{m}$ for v_1 in the formula with number m, that is, in $p(v_1)$, so that $s(\bar{m}, \bar{m}) = \gamma[p(\bar{m})]$. Now $p(\bar{m}) = \neg w(s(\bar{m}, \bar{m}))$ is true iff the formula with number $s(\bar{m}, \bar{m})$ is not true, that is, iff $p(\bar{m})$ is not true. This contradiction shows that L cannot contain both $s(v_1, v_2) = v_3$ and $w(v_1)$. This proves the following:

TARSKI'S THEOREM. If the theory T is such that there exists a formula $s(v_1, v_2) = v_3$ expressing substitution, then the property of being a true formula of T is not expressible in T.

The condition on T is modest. We could with little pains construct the formula $s(v_1, v_2) = v_3$ explicitly, and adjoin to A_0 and A_1 a finite set A_2 of recursive definitions for all auxiliary arithmetic functions appearing in $s(v_1, v_2)$. Then we conclude that, if $A_0 \cup A_1 \cup A_2 \subseteq T$, the truth of a formula in T is not expressible in T.

The conclusion of Tarski's Theorem is not intuitively surprising: it is hard to imagine how one would go about expressing within T the semantic concept of being a true formula of T. After this analysis then, there remains in the Liar Paradox nothing unsettling.

GÖDEL'S INCOMPLETENESS THEOREM

We obtain first a weak form of the Incompleteness Theorem, and later a stronger form. We repeat our hypothesis on A, that $s(v_1, v_2) = v_3$ and $b(v_1, v_2)$ express the intended meanings in T.

INCOMPLETENESS THEOREM. If the theory T is valid, it is not complete.

The proof is by the same diagonal argument, but now with the formula $t(v_1) = \mathsf{E}v_2 b(v_2, v_1)$, which is known to express provability, in place of the formula $w(v_1)$. If we define $p(v_1) = \neg t(s(v_1, v_1))$ and set $m = \gamma[p(v_1)]$, then again $s(\overline{m}, \overline{m}) = \gamma[p(\overline{m})]$. Now $p(m)$ is true iff $s(\overline{m}, \overline{m})$ is not the number of a provable formula, that is, iff $p(\overline{m})$ is not provable. Thus, if $p(\overline{m})$ were provable it would be untrue, contrary to the assumption that T is valid, and we conclude that $p(\overline{m})$ is unprovable but true. Finally, since $p(\overline{m})$ is true, $\neg p(\overline{m})$ is not true, and, by the validity of T, $\neg p(\overline{m})$ is not provable.

COROLLARY. The theory T', comprising all true formulas of arithmetic, is not decidable.

If T' were decidable we could axiomatize it, taking for our set A of axioms the set T' itself. The Incompleteness Theorem now implies that T' is not complete, whereas T', defined by a single standard model, must in fact be complete.

These two theorems express the main intuitive content of the assertions that ordinary arithmetic is neither decidable nor axiomatizable. However both of these results, with their reference to validity, have a semantic component. We shall next obtain sharper forms of these theorems that are purely syntactical.

DECIDABILITY AND CHURCH'S THEOREM

Consider again a formula $p(v_1, \ldots, v_n)$ of L that expresses a property $P(m_1, \ldots, m_n)$ of natural numbers. Suppose the formula p is *definite* in the sense that, for arbitrary natural numbers $m_1, \ldots, m_n$, the formula $p(\bar{m}_1, \ldots, \bar{m}_n)$ is provable iff it is true, and the same for the negation of this formula. Given numbers $m_1, \ldots, m_n$, either $p(\bar{m}_1, \ldots, \bar{m}_n)$ or its negation is true, whence one or the other has a proof. By running in alphabetical order through all proofs, we are assured of finding a proof either of this formula or its negations, and thus deciding whether $P(m_1, \ldots, m_n)$ holds or fails. Suppose conversely that the property P is decidable in an intuitive sense. Then there exists an algorithm, or scheme of computation, which applied to a set of arguments $m_1, \ldots, m_n$, tells us whether $P(m_1, \ldots, m_n)$ holds or fails. This algorithm should then be expressible in T, by a formula $p(v_1, \ldots, v_n)$ such that $p(\bar{m}_1, \ldots, \bar{m}_n)$ expresses that $P(m_1, \ldots, m_n)$ holds, and which carries with it a proof either of $p(\bar{m}_1, \ldots, \bar{m}_n)$ or of its negation.

These are our informal reasons for now defining a property P of natural numbers to be *decidable* if it is expressible, in some finitely axiomatizable theory T, by a definite formula p.

The majority of our syntactic concepts are decidable in the intuitive sense, and we should expect the corresponding formulas expressing them, in particular the formulas $b(v_1, v_2)$ and $s(v_1, v_2) = v_3$, to be definite. A full proof of this would require an exact description of these formulas; we shall indicate here only one crucial element of such a proof.

An occurrence of a quantifier in a formula is called *bounded* if it begins a subformula of one of the two forms $\mathsf{A}x[x \leq t \supset p]$ or $\mathsf{E}x[x \leq t \wedge p]$, where $x \leq y$ is an abbreviation for $\mathsf{E}z(x + z = y)$ and t is a term in which x does not occur free. It is intuitively plausible that a decidable property expressed by a formula $p(v_1, \ldots, v_n)$ of the form $\mathsf{A}xq(x, v_1, \ldots, v_n)$ or $\mathsf{E}xq(x, v_1, \ldots, v_n)$, with q definite, should be expressible with a bounded quantifier. For the case at hand, this can be verified by explicitly describing such expressions; in particular, $b(v_1, v_2)$ and $s(v_1, v_2) = v_3$ can be replaced by equivalent formulas containing only bounded quantifiers. We now consider a formula $p(v_1, \ldots, v_n) = \mathsf{A}x[x \leq t(v_1, \ldots, v_n) \supset q(x, v_1, \ldots, v_n)]$ where x does not occur free in t and the formulas $t(v_1, \ldots, v_n) = v_{n+1}$ and $q(v_1, \ldots, v_{n+1})$ are definite. If $m_1, \ldots, m_n$ are given, the solution m of $t(\overline{m}_1, \ldots, \overline{m}_n) = \overline{m}$ can be found by search, and the formula $p(\overline{m}_1, \ldots, \overline{m}_n)$ is evidently equivalent to the conjunction $q(\overline{0}, \overline{m}_1, \ldots, \overline{m}_n) \wedge \ldots \wedge q(\overline{m}, \overline{m}_1, \ldots, \overline{m}_n)$. Since the formula q is definite, it follows that p is; and a similar argument applies for a bounded existential quantifier. By this means one shows that a formula with only bounded quantifiers is definite, and hence that $b(v_1, v_2)$ and $s(v_1, v_2) = v_3$ are definite.

There is no reason to believe that an arithmetical function $f(v_1)$ can be found such that, given the Gödel number m of a theorem, $f(m)$ is a bound for the length of the shortest proof. That is, there is no evident way to replace the first quantifier in the formula $t(v_1) = \mathsf{E}v_2 b(v_2, v_1)$ by a bounded quantifier, and one is led to the suspicion that $t(v_1)$ is not definite and, therefore, the set T of theorems is not decidable. This is the case.

PROPOSITION. If $b(v_1, v_2)$ and $s(v_1, v_2) = v_3$ are definite formulas in the theory T, then T is undecidable.

The proof follows again the pattern of the Liar Paradox. Taking $p(v_1) = \neg t(s(v_1, v_1))$ and $m = \gamma[p(v_1)]$ as before, we again have that $p(\overline{m})$ is true iff it is not provable. On the other hand, if $t(v_1)$ were definite, we should have that $p(\overline{m}) = \neg t(s(\overline{m}, \overline{m})$ is true iff it is provable, a contradiction.

CHURCH'S THEOREM. The set of all valid formulas of the predicate logic is not decidable.

To prove this, we take T in the proposition as economically as possible. In order to ensure that $b(v_1, v_2)$ and $s(v_1, v_2) = v_3$ are definite, we may require in L various function symbols for auxiliary functions used in constructing these two formulas; then we require various axioms in A, other than those in $A_0 \cup A_1$, in the form of recursive definitions of these function symbols, to ensure that they receive the correct interpretation. But, in all, we can suppose that L has only finitely many function and relation symbols, and that $A = A_0 \cup A_1 \cup A_2$ where A_2 is finite. Moreover, since L contains only finitely many function and relation symbols, the set $A_=$ of axioms for identity can be taken to be finite. Let a be the conjunction of all formulas in the finite set $A_= \cup A_1 \cup A_2$. Then $A \models p$ iff $\models a \supset p$, that is, a formula p belongs to T iff $a \supset p$ is a valid formula of the predicate calculus. Thus decidability of the predicate logic would imply that of T, and Church's Theorem follows.

THE UNPROVABILITY OF CONSISTENCY

We first strengthen the Incompleteness Theorem to a purely syntactical form.

Once again we take $p(v_1) = \neg \mathrm{E} v_2 b(v_2, s(v_1, v_1))$ and $m = \gamma[p(v_1)]$. We prove two lemmas.

LEMMA. If T is consistent, then $p(\bar{m})$ is not provable.

Suppose $p(\bar{m})$ provable. Then it has a proof, with some Gödel number n, and, since $\gamma[p(\bar{m})] = s(\bar{m}, \bar{m})$, the formula $b(\bar{n}, s(\bar{m}, \bar{m}))$ expressing that n is the number of a proof of $p(\bar{m})$ is true. Since $b(v_1, v_2)$ is definite, this implies that $b(\bar{n}, s(\bar{m}, \bar{m}))$ is provable, whence $\mathrm{E} v_2 b(v_2, s(\bar{m}, \bar{m}))$ is provable. Since $p(\bar{m})$, the negation of this last formula, is also provable, we conclude that T is inconsistent.

A theory T is called *ω-consistent* if there is no formula $q(v_1)$ such that T contains the formula $\mathrm{E} x q(x)$ and yet all the formulas $\neg q(\bar{n})$ for n in N. Evidently any theory valid in the domain N is ω-consistent; however, in general, ω-consistency is stronger than consistency.

LEMMA. If T is ω-consistent, then $\neg p(\bar{m})$ is not provable.

Suppose $\neg p(\bar{m})$ provable. Since T is consistent, $p(\bar{m})$ is not provable, and, for every number n, n is not the number of a proof for $p(\bar{m})$, that is, $\neg b(\bar{n}, s(\bar{m}, \bar{m}))$ is true. Since $b(v_1, v_2)$ is definite, it follows that, for each n, $\neg b(\bar{n}, s(\bar{m}, \bar{m}))$ is provable. From the ω-consistency of T, we conclude that $\mathrm{E} x b(x, s(\bar{m}, \bar{m}))$ is not provable, hence that $\neg p(\bar{m}) = \neg \neg \mathrm{E} x b(x, s(\bar{m}, \bar{m}))$ is not provable, which contradicts our hypothesis.

We conclude that, if T is ω-consistent, then neither $p(\overline{m})$ nor $\neg p(\overline{m})$ is provable, and hence that T is incomplete. In fact, Rosser has refined the argument to obtain the same conclusion under the weaker assumption that T is merely consistent. For the record, we state the result in this stronger form.

INCOMPLETENESS THEOREM (Syntactic form). If T is a theory in which $b(v_1, v_2)$ and $s(v_1, v_2) = v_3$ are definite, then T is incomplete.

This result can be made more explicit by taking T to be defined by a specific set A of axioms, as before.

We conclude with one more theorem of Gödel, which is perhaps the most far-reaching in its implications for the foundations of mathematics.

THEOREM. Let T be a theory in which $b(v_1, v_2)$ and $s(v_1, v_2) = v_3$ are definite. Then T contains sentences expressing the fact that T is consistent, but no such sentence is provable in T.

Since $\gamma[0] = 4$, the sentence $c = \neg \mathrm{E}xb(x, \overline{4})$ expresses that the sentence 0 is not provable, that is, that T is consistent. In support of the first lemma above, we gave a proof that the consistency of T implied the unprovability of $p(\overline{m})$, and hence the truth of $p(\overline{m})$, which asserts the unprovability of $p(\overline{m})$. If d is the Gödel number of the formula $c \supset p(\overline{m})$, then, since this formula has a proof with some Gödel number h, the formula $b(\overline{h}, \overline{d})$ is true for some natural number h. If c were provable, then $b(\overline{k}, \overline{\gamma[c]})$ would be true for some number k, and it would be easy to conclude that some number j were the number of a proof of $p(\overline{m})$. But T is consistent, since by hypothesis $b(v_1, v_2)$ is definite in T, and this implies that $p(\overline{m})$ is not provable, a contradiction.

BIBLIOGRAPHY

BENACERRAF, P., and H. PUTNAM. *Philosophy of Mathematics: Selected Readings,* Englewood Cliffs, 1964.

CHURCH, A. *Mathematical Logic I,* Princeton, 1956.

DAVIS, M. *Computability and Unsolvability,* New York, 1958.

FRAENKEL, A. *Abstract Set Theory,* Amsterdam, 1961.

HALMOS, P. R. *Algebraic Logic,* New York, 1962.

HENKIN, L. "The completeness of the first-order functional calculus," *Jour. Symbolic Logic,* v. *14,* pp. 159–166, 1949.

HENKIN, L., and A. TARSKI. "Cylindric algebras," *Proc. Symposia Pure Math.,* v. *2,* pp. 83–113, Providence, 1961.

HEYTING, A. *Intuitionism,* Amsterdam, 1956.

KLEENE, S. C. *Introduction to Metamathematics,* New York, 1952.

KRIPKE, S. A. "Semantical analysis of modal logic I: Normal modal propositional calculi," *Zeitschrift Math. Logik Grundlagen Math.,* v. *9,* pp. 67–96, 1963.

LORENZEN, P. *Metamathematik,* Mannheim, 1962.

NAGEL, E., and J.R. NEWMAN. *Gödel's Proof,* London, 1959.

RASIOWA, H., and R. SIKORSKI. "On the Gentzen theorem," *Fundamenta Math.,* v. *58,* pp. 59–69, 1960.

ROBINSON, A. *Introduction to Model Theory and the Metamathematics of Algebra,* Amsterdam, 1963.

ROGERS, H., Jr. "An example in mathematical logic," *Amer. Math. Monthly,* v. *70,* pp. 929–945, 1963.

TARSKI, A. "The semantic conception of truth," *Philos. Phenomenological Research,* v. *4,* pp. 13–47, 1944.

TARSKI, A. *A Decision Method for Elementary Algebra and Geometry,* Berkeley and Los Angeles, 1951.

TARSKI, A., A. MOSTOWSKI, and R. M. ROBINSON. *Undecidable Theories,* Amsterdam, 1953.

WILDER, R. L. *Introduction to the Foundations of Mathematics,* New York, 1952.

INDEX OF NAMES

INDEX OF TERMS